W9-CFX-335

PRENTICE-HALL FOUNDATIONS OF MODERN BIOLOGY SERIES

William D. McElroy and Carl P. Swanson, Editors

NEW VOLUME

Chemical Background for the Biological Sciences, Emil H. White

SECOND EDITIONS

The Cell, Carl P. Swanson

Cell Physiology and Biochemistry, William D. McElroy

Heredity, David M. Bonner and Stanley E. Mills

Adaptation, Bruce Wallace and Adrian M. Srb

Growth and Development, Maurice Sussman

Animal Physiology, Knut Schmidt-Nielsen

Animal Diversity, Earl D. Hanson

Animal Behavior, V. G. Dethier and Eliot Stellar

The Life of the Green Plant, Arthur W. Galston

The Plant Kingdom, Harold C. Bold

Man in Nature, Marston Bates

HAROLD C. BOLD   *The University of Texas*

Englewood Cliffs, N. J.   **PRENTICE-HALL, INC.**

The Plant Kingdom

SECOND EDITION

FOUNDATIONS OF MODERN BIOLOGY SERIES

THE PLANT KINGDOM, SECOND EDITION, *Harold C. Bold*

FOUNDATIONS OF MODERN BIOLOGY SERIES

William D. McElroy and Carl P. Swanson, Editors

Design by Walter Behnke

Drawings by Felix Cooper

Second printing..........June, 1965

PRENTICE-HALL INTERNATIONAL, INC., *London*
PRENTICE-HALL OF AUSTRALIA, PTY., LTD., *Sydney*
PRENTICE-HALL OF CANADA, LTD., *Toronto*
PRENTICE-HALL OF INDIA PVT., LTD., *New Delhi*
PRENTICE-HALL OF JAPAN, INC., *Tokyo*

C-68034(p)   *C-68035(c)*

TO   M. D. B.

The writer wishes to express his appreciation to the following who have helped him in the preparation of this book: Professors Robert L. Airth, Const. J. Alexopoulos, Ralph E. Alston, Henry N. Andrews, Jr., Walter V. Brown, William K. Davis, Charles Heimsch, Donald A. Larson, Marshall C. Johnston, Edwin B. Matzke, and B. L. Turner; Drs. T. R. Deason, L. R. Hoffman, and B. C. Parker; and Messrs. R. Malcolm Brown, Jr., and Geza Knipfer.

Foundations
of Modern Biology
Series

PREFACE TO THE FIRST EDITION

The science of biology today is *not* the same science of fifty twenty-five, or even ten years ago. Today's accelerated pace of research, aided by new instruments, techniques, and points of view, imparts to biology a rapidly changing character as discoveries pile one on top of the other. All of us are aware, however, that each new and important discovery is not just a mere addition to our knowledge; it also throws our established beliefs into question, and forces us constantly to reappraise and often to reshape the foundations upon which biology rests. An adequate presentation of the dynamic state of modern biology is, therefore, a formidable task and a challenge worthy of our best teachers.

The authors of this series believe that a new approach to the organization of the subject matter of biology is urgently needed to meet this challenge, an approach that introduces the student to biology as a growing, active science, and that also *permits each teacher of biology to determine the level and structure of his own course*. A single textbook cannot provide such flexibility, and it is the author's strong conviction that these student needs and teacher prerogatives can best be met by a series of short, inexpensive, well-written, and well-illustrated books so planned as to encompass those areas of study central to an understanding of the content, state, and direction of modern biology. The FOUNDATIONS OF MODERN BIOLOGY SERIES represents the translation of these ideas into print, with each volume being complete in itself yet at the same time serving as an integral part of the series as a whole.

PREFACE TO THE SECOND EDITION

The first edition of the FOUNDATIONS OF MODERN BIOLOGY SERIES represented a marked departure from the traditions of textbook writing. The enthusiastic acceptance of the Series by teachers of biology, here and abroad, has been most heartening, and confirms our belief that there was a long-felt need for flexible teaching units based on current views and concepts. The second edition of all volumes in the Series retains the earlier flexibility, eliminates certain unnecessary overlaps of content, introduces new and relevant information, and provides more meaningful illustrative material.

The Series has also been strengthened by the inclusion of a new volume, *Chemical Background for the Biological Sciences* by Dr. Emil White. The dependence of modern biology on a sound foundation in physics and chemistry is obvious; this volume is designed to provide the necessary background in these areas.

In preparing the second edition of the Series, the authors and editors gratefully acknowledge the many constructive criticisms that have been made by hundreds of teaching biologists. Their interest and aid have made the task of writing more a pleasure than a burden.

Contents

ONE   **THE UNITY AND DIVERSITY OF PLANTS,**   *1*

> *Classification of Plants.   Unity vs. Diversity of Plants.*

TWO   **THE ALGAE,**   *7*

> *Form and Organization in Algae.   Cellular Organization.   Reproduction in Algae.   Notes on Some Divisions of Algae.*

THREE   **BACTERIA, SLIME MOLDS, AND FUNGI,**   *20*

> *The Bacteria.   The Slime Molds (Myxomycetes).   The Fungi.*

FOUR   **NONVASCULAR LAND PLANTS: MOSSES AND LIVERWORTS,**   *38*

> *Mosses.   Liverworts.*

FIVE   **THE STRUCTURE OF VASCULAR PLANTS,**   *46*

> *Ontogeny of Axes (Stems and Roots).   Morphology of Leaves.*

ix

SIX   **SEEDLESS VASCULAR PLANTS I,**   *57*

  Psilophytes.   Club   and   Spike   "Mosses."   Arthrophytes.

SEVEN   **SEEDLESS VASCULAR PLANTS II: THE FERNS,**   *70*

  Summary of Seedless Vascular Plants.

EIGHT   **GYMNOSPERMOUS SEED PLANTS,**   *77*

  Reproduction in Gymnospermous Seed Plants.   Representative Gymnospermous Seed Plants.

NINE   **THE FLOWERING PLANTS, OR ANGIOSPERMS,**   *87*

  The Gross Morphology of Flowers.   The Reproductive Process in Angiosperms.

TEN   **SUMMARY,**   *102*

  Organization of the Plant Body.   Reproduction.   Development of Plants in Time; Classification.

SELECTED READINGS,   *111*

INDEX,   *112*

The Unity
and Diversity
of Plants

CHAPTER ONE

Our environment is characterized by richly diversified plant life on which we are dependent for our very existence. The air we breathe contains a continuously adequate level of oxygen only because it is so maintained by green, chlorophyllous plants. Furthermore, plants, both aquatic and terrestrial, are the foundation of the food chain for the animal kingdom. Their protoplasm and its products are the basic sources of the energy and the building blocks with which animal protoplasm is synthesized. The more subtle activities of certain achlorophyllous plants, the bacteria and fungi, are also of great significance in the biological world.

At first glance, we are likely to be impressed with the diversity of plants that populate the earth. The green scum on certain ponds, the duckweed on others, the lichens, fungi, mosses, ferns, conifers, and flowering plants, some of which populate even the most inhospitable areas of the earth, both land and sea—all are elements of this diversity and form the subject matter of the present volume. We shall survey this variety and emphasize the important biological principles that are particularly well illustrated by each of the several plant groups. Such questions as the origin of life, its diversity, and its interrelationships, which can be demonstrated among our present-day organisms, will also be considered. We shall devote some attention as well to extinct plants known to us only as fossil remains. These topics may best be discussed in connection with the plants themselves. One topic, however, the classification of plants, requires immediate consideration.

CLASSIFICATION OF PLANTS

Classifications of organisms are man-made. There are two types of classification systems of living organisms. The first, and oldest, type is called *artificial:* In artificial systems organisms are grouped together on the basis of convenience. Such groupings do not imply actual kinship. Examples of this type of classification are the division of plants into beneficial and harmful, into herbaceous and woody, or into evergreen and deciduous. As students of plant structure, known as morphologists, became impressed with the basic similarity in the body plans of certain plants, they began to group them into *natural,* or *phylogenetic,* systems, in which the several categories in fact implied actual kinship. Natural classifications, which are designed to indicate relationship among living organisms, are based on carefully evaluated evidence of several types. The more important of these are the fossil record, geographical distribution, and comparative studies of living plants, including structure, function, biochemistry, development, and chromosomal and genic constitution.

Darwin's publication of *The Origin of Species* in 1859 gave great impetus to such classifications. Even today, classifications differ with the classifiers' appraisals of available evidences of relationship, evidences sought in the comparative study of both living and fossil plants. Our knowledge of the latter, of course, will at best always be incomplete. Classifications of plants (and animals), therefore, are in a state of flux and are subject to criticism and disagreement, for they represent only approximations and are continually being modified as new evidence for or against a postulated relationship between groups is uncovered. Several systems of classification of plants are summarized comparatively in Table 1-1. In addition, this table lists the common, anglicized names for the several groups and estimates of the numbers of species in each. The presence of three systems of classification in Table 1-1 is of itself good evidence that agreement has not been reached regarding the degree of relationship among plants. Classification of plants, like science itself, is not static, but subject to modification as new data emerge. Of course, you should *not* memorize this table of classifications, but should use it as a reference to alternative schemes of classification of the plants treated in Chapters 2 to 9 and in other books.

UNITY VS. DIVERSITY OF PLANTS

As Table 1-1 indicates, certain groups of plants have vernacular names, such as *algae, fungi, bacteria, mosses, ferns, seed plants,* and *flowering*

Table 1-1
A COMPARATIVE SUMMARY OF SOME CLASSIFICATIONS OF THE PLANT KINGDOM [1]

The arrows indicate the fate of taxa in successively more modern systems of classification. When the name of a group is used later at a higher rank, as, for example, in the change from Chlorophyceae to Chlorophyta, the name of the lower group usually is retained as a subsidiary under the higher.

Eichler, 1883 (and modifications)	Tippo, 1942	Bold, 1956	Common Name	Approximate Number of Species
PLANT KINGDOM →	PLANT KINGDOM →	PLANT KINGDOM		
A. CRYPTOGAMAE →	Abandoned	→ Abandoned		
DIVISION 1. THALLOPHYTA →	SUB-KINGDOM 1. THALLOPHYTA →	Abandoned		
Class 1. Algae →	Abandoned			
Cyanophyceae →	PHYLUM [2] 1. CYANOPHYTA →	DIVISION 1. CYANOPHYTA		
Chlorophyceae →	PHYLUM 2. CHLOROPHYTA →	DIVISION 2. CHLOROPHYTA		
	PHYLUM 3. EUGLENOPHYTA →	DIVISION 3. EUGLENOPHYTA		
		DIVISION 4. CHAROPHYTA	Algae	(19,000)
Phaeophyceae →	PHYLUM 4. PHAEOPHYTA →	DIVISION 5. PHAEOPHYTA		
Rhodophyceae →	PHYLUM 5. RHODOPHYTA →	DIVISION 6. RHODOPHYTA		
Diatomeae →	PHYLUM 6. CHRYSOPHYTA →	DIVISION 7. CHRYSOPHYTA		
	PHYLUM 7. PYRROPHYTA →	DIVISION 8. PYRROPHYTA		
Class 2. Fungi →	Abandoned			
Schizomycetes →	PHYLUM 8. SCHIZOMYCOPHYTA →	DIVISION 9. SCHIZOMYCOTA		
	PHYLUM 9. MYXOMYCOPHYTA →	DIVISION 10. MYXOMYCOTA		
Eumycetes →	PHYLUM 10. EUMYCOPHYTA →	Abandoned	Fungi (*Sensu lato*)	(42,000)
	Class 1. Phycomycetes →	DIVISION 11. PHYCOMYCOTA		
	Class 2. Ascomycetes →	DIVISION 12. ASCOMYCOTA		
Lichens →	Class 3. Basidiomycetes →	DIVISION 13. BASIDIOMYCOTA		
	SUB-KINGDOM 2. EMBRYOPHYTA →	Abandoned		
DIVISION 2. BRYOPHYTA →	PHYLUM 11. BRYOPHYTA			
Class 1. Hepaticae →	Class 1. Hepaticae →	DIVISION 14. HEPATOPHYTA	Liverworts	(9,000)
Class 2. Musci →	Class 2. Musci →	DIVISION 15. BRYOPHYTA	Mosses	(14,000)
DIVISION 3. PTERIDOPHYTA →	Abandoned			
	PHYLUM 12. TRACHEOPHYTA →	Abandoned		
	Sub-phylum 1. Psilopsida →	DIVISION 16. PSILOPHYTA	Psilophytes	(4)
Class 1. Lycopodinae →	Sub-phylum 2. Lycopsida →	DIVISION 17. MICROPHYLLOPHYTA	Club Mosses	(1,000)
Class 2. Equisetinae →	Sub-phylum 3. Sphenopsida →	DIVISION 18. ARTHROPHYTA	Horsetails and Sphenopsids	(25)
	Sub-phylum 4. Pteropsida →	Abandoned		
Class 3. Filicinae →	Class 1. Filicinae →	DIVISION 19. PTEROPHYTA	Ferns	(9,500)
B. PHANEROGAMAE →	Abandoned			
DIVISION 4. SPERMATOPHYTA →	Abandoned			
Class 1. Gymnospermae →	Class 2. Gymnospermae →	Abandoned		
	Sub-class 1. Cycadophytae →	DIVISION 20. CYCADOPHYTA	Cycads	(100)
		DIVISION 21. GINKGOPHYTA	Maidenhair Tree (Ginkgo)	(1)
	Sub-class 2. Coniferophytae →	DIVISION 22. CONIFEROPHYTA	Conifers	(550)
		DIVISION 23. GNETOPHYTA	(No common, inclusive name)	(71)
Class 2. Angiospermae →	Class 3. Angiospermae →	DIVISION 24. ANTHOPHYTA	Flowering plants	(250,000)
			Approximate Total	(850,000)

[1] Only groups with currently living plants are included.

[2] Although approximately equivalent to "Division," "Phylum" is not recognized as a category by the International Code of Botanical Nomenclature.

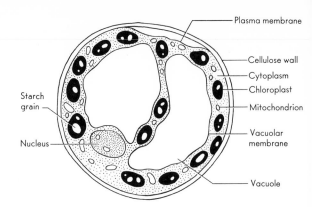

Plasma membrane

Cellulose wall

Cytoplasm

Chloroplast

Mitochondrion

Vacuolar membrane

Vacuole

Starch grain

Nucleus

Fig. 1-1. Generalized structure of a plant cell, the vacuoles of which are not completely filled with fluid (cell sap).

plants. Examples of these are illustrated in the chapters that follow. In considering such an assemblage of plants, one is at once impressed by their diversity in habitat and structure, and by their seeming diversity of function. The diversity of these organisms is, indeed, the subject matter of the present volume, but there are also common attributes that are shared nearly universally by living organisms. Some of these unifying attributes of plants (and animals) are: (1) *cellular organization;* (2) *metabolic phenomena;* (3) *sexual reproduction;* (4) *genetic phenomena;* and (5) *adaptation.*

CELLULAR ORGANIZATION.* In 1839, the botanist M. J. Schleiden and the zoologist Theodor Schwann published their theory that the cell (Fig. 1-1) is the universal unit of organization in plants and animals. They arrived at this conclusion as a result of numerous studies by investigators working with the light microscope from the time of its invention in 1590. This basic cell theory has become the generally accepted explanation of the organization of organisms. Furthermore, with the exception of blue-green algae and bacteria (see p. 22), such cellular components as nuclei, nuclear membranes, cytoplasm, mitochondria, Golgi bodies, and endoplasmic reticulum are present in all plant and animal cells ever studied.

METABOLISM. The many chemical activities carried on by living organisms, collectively called *metabolism,* offer additional evidence of unity. Such processes as energy release in respiration seem to be universally the same in living organisms, as do many of the pathways of chemical synthesis and degradation.† Further, many *enzymes,* the catalysts of metabolic processes in living organisms, are similar in various types of protoplasm.

SEXUAL REPRODUCTION. No matter how diverse organisms may be (algae, elephants, daffodils, or human beings), four phenomena are almost always involved in *sexual reproduction,* namely, the union of cells, the union of their nuclei,** the intermingling of two sets of nuclear components

---

* See also in this series C. P. Swanson, *The Cell,* 2nd ed. (Englewood Cliffs, N. J.: Prentice-Hall, 1964).

† See also in this series W. D. McElroy, *Cellular Physiology and Biochemistry,* 2nd ed. (Englewood Cliffs, N. J.: Prentice-Hall, 1964).

** In some organisms, the nuclei merely remain side by side, and the chromosomes do not become associated until the zygote divides.

5

(chromosomes with their genetic materials), and, finally, their reassort-ment at *meiosis,* or "reduction division." These four are connected with another unifying principle, the phenomenon of inheritance, the laws of which are the province of genetics.* In the plant kingdom only blue-green algae and the euglenoids seem to lack sexual reproduction.

GENETIC PHENOMENA. The life of each individual cell, the differentia-tion of cells in the development of complex multicellular organisms, and, finally, the transmission of hereditary traits are governed—in *all* organisms —by their deoxyribonucleic acid (DNA) in interaction with the cytoplasm. The specific pattern of organization is responsible for the structural and functional attributes of the cell, as they develop in a given environment.

ADAPTATION. This is another manifestation of the unity of living or-ganisms. Adaptation is the capacity of organisms both individually and as continuing, sexually reproducing populations to get along in their envi-ronment. Adaptations are both morphological (structural) and physiologi-cal (functional), two aspects of organisms that are usually intimately con-nected. Living things are attuned to their environment; those that are not, become extinct.†

How, then, are the diversities among living organisms to be reconciled with the equally apparent and striking similarities just enumerated? Modern biology answers this seeming paradox with the concept of *organic evolu-tion.*** According to this explanation, diversity has arisen secondarily. It is deviation from original unity and has occurred during the approximately two billion years that life has probably existed on this planet. The living organisms we see about us are the present actors on an ancient stage. With lapse of time, the settings have changed and so have the actors. They have become transformed in some respects as they acted; many have dropped out. Many others have become so changed over the ages through selection and new combinations of mutations as to be scarcely recognizable, and we are thus driven to speculate regarding their origin. That such spontaneously occurring changes, or *mutations,* have occurred and are oc-curring in living organisms is no longer subject to doubt. We can observe them taking place on a small scale in nature at present and we can induce them to occur by suitable stimuli such as irradiation and chemical agents. During many generations of sexually breeding populations, certain com-binations of mutations became selected and dominant, so that in time the species changed. This is postulated to be the fundamental explanation of the diversity of present-day organisms and the cause of their modification from their ancestors. Since the sequence of occurrence and inheritance of

* See also in this series D. M. Bonner, *Heredity,* 2nd ed. (Englewood Cliffs, N. J.: Prentice-Hall, 1964).

† See also in this series B. Wallace and A. M. Srb, *Adaptation,* 2nd ed. (Engle-wood Cliffs, N. J.: Prentice-Hall, 1964).

** See also in this series E. D. Hanson, *Animal Diversity,* 2nd ed. (Englewood Cliffs, N. J.: Prentice-Hall, 1964).

many of the changes cannot be followed completely and unequivocally, the story of the *course* of organic evolution in the past will probably remain incomplete. The point to note here is that a survey of diverse types of plants may tend to obscure the fact that present diversity sprang from earlier unity.

In such considerations, we are finally brought face-to-face with the ultimate question of the origin of life itself. Did it arise but once or more than once? How was the first life organized? What was the nature of its nutritive and metabolic processes? For a long time, it was taken for granted that answers to these questions must be relegated to the realm of speculation, but recent and significant experiments indicate that the origin of life may be subject to experimental analyses. In a series of investigations wherein various mixtures of gases—namely, methane, ammonia, hydrogen, and water vapor—were enclosed in chambers in which electricity was discharged, the production of amino acids, which are building units in the proteins of living organisms, was achieved in entirely nonliving systems. Thus the distinction between the inorganic and the organic has become irrelevant.

Early speculators usually postulated that the most primitive living organisms must have been those that could thrive in an environment which contained only inorganic, low-energy compounds. Accordingly, such organisms must have possessed a tremendous range of enzymes, to convert such substances into protoplasm. Quite the opposite view has become widely accepted during the last two decades. This view postulates that the first organisms lived in a medium supplied with complex, high-energy-containing molecules, which they could utilize directly or with a minimum of change. As the availability of these complex substances became critical, the hypothesis runs, alternate pathways of synthesis of protoplasm evolved. These enabled primitive organisms to build up their substance from increasingly less complex building units.

According to one point of view, chlorophyll-containing, photosynthetic organisms are less primitive than nongreen ones like most bacteria, fungi, and animals. On the other hand, it is quite possible that some nonchlorophyllous organisms evolved from green organisms by losing their ability to produce chlorophyll. This latter change can be experimentally produced in certain unicellular algae by high temperature. Comparative studies of the nutrition of microorganisms are shedding a good deal of light on these questions. The origin and relationships of diverse living organisms, their variations in structure, nutrition, and metabolism, constitute the subject matter of organic evolution, which postulates that living things are related to one another because of descent from a common ancestry. It is the purpose of the present volume to survey these diversities in orderly fashion and thus to give you some insight into the range and activities of members of the plant kingdom.

The Algae

Although no one can describe the organization of primitive life with absolute certainty, the fossil record indicates strongly that organisms much like our modern algae lived more than a billion and a half years ago. This is *not* to state categorically that algae were the earliest living organisms. The fossil record is incomplete and always will be, but there is every indication that algae are ancient plants, at least some of which have persisted with little modification from their progenitors. For this reason and because of the relative simplicity of most algae, we shall begin our survey of the diversity of the plant kingdom with them. Furthermore, algae provide elegant material for laboratory demonstrations of many fundamental biological phenomena.

What are algae? Where do they grow? What do they do and what are they good for? In the following pages we shall ask and attempt to answer these questions about algae (and later about every group of plants we consider). To the layman, algae are "pond scums," "sea weeds" (even when they grow in fresh water!), and, too often, "mosses." To the biologist, they are chlorophyll-bearing organisms that may have

7

gametes (see p. 14) but no specialized sex organs, or unicellular sex organs, or multicellular sex organs in which every cell forms a gamete. In these respects, they differ from all other green plants. This definition may seem technical, but it is so of necessity, for science in its dedication to accuracy requires strict definition.

Algae are both marine and fresh-water, and they also occur on and within soil and on moist stones and wood, as well as in association with fungi and certain animals. With respect to "what they do" and "what they are good for," algae are of paramount importance as primary producers of energy-rich compounds that form the basis of the food cycle of all aquatic animal life. In this connection, the planktonic (water-suspended) algae are especially important, since they serve as food for many animals. It has been estimated, for example, that about 90 per cent of the photosynthesis on earth is carried on by aquatic plants; the planktonic algae are primarily responsible for this. Furthermore, algae oxygenate their habitat while they are photosynthesizing, thus increasing the level of dissolved oxygen in their immediate environment. In addition, certain blue-green algae —like some bacteria, but unlike most other plants—can employ gaseous nitrogen from the atmosphere in building their protoplasm, and in this way they contribute significantly to the nitrogenous compounds in water and in soils where they live. Their activity is called *nitrogen fixation*.

In addition to these basic biological activities, algae have proved useful to man in a number of ways. More than 70 species of marine algae (sea weeds) are used as food, mostly by oriental peoples, although several of the red algae are sold as food in the United States. Certain brown and red marine algae produce large amounts of hydrocolloids (water-holding substances) as intercellular secretions. Of these, *algin* (of brown algae) and *carrageenin* (of red algae) are used commercially. These hydrocolloidal substances are extracted from the algae, dried, and powdered. Upon rehydration, they are used in chocolate milk, ice cream, prepared icings and fillings, toothpaste, etc.

Another type of algae, the *diatoms* (Fig. 2-9), which populated ancient seas (and which occur in oceans today), also are of value. The cells of ancient diatoms, covered with siliceous walls, settled to the bottom at the cells' death, the walls being deposited in extensive layers of "diatomaceous earth," which is now of use in filtration, in insulation, as an ingredient in paint, and as a fine abrasive in silver polish.

In some instances, however, algae may become offensive to the eye or nose, or in still other ways. The appearance of a great concentration of algae under favorable conditions (for them) produces "water blooms," which render recreational bodies of water temporarily unusable. The occurrence of large mats of floating algae in fishponds may result in the death of many fish from lack of oxygen, since at night the algae not only are in competition with the fish for this gas but form a blanket which reduces oxygenation of the water from the atmosphere. There are indications too that toxic products from algae in water blooms may poison livestock and fish. The familiar phenomena of the so-called "red tides" that kill fish are associated with the abundance of an alga, *Gonyaulax*. Finally we must note at this point one further aspect of the use of algae, namely, their increasing importance in basic biological research, in such areas as sexuality, metabolism, genetics, etc. This is true especially of the unicellular algae, because of their small size and the ease and rapidity with which large populations may be grown.

Let us now turn from general considerations to more specific data concerning algae. Hundreds of genera * of algae are known, and our knowledge of them is constantly being augmented. In older systems of classification (Table 1-1), the algae were considered to be a uniform group, but of late "Algae" has been abandoned as a formal taxon in classification, and the group has been broken up into a number of divisions on the basis of the diversity of certain structural and biochemical attributes. These are summarized in Table 2-1. It should be apparent from this table that the several groups of algae differ in pigmentation, food reserves, wall composition, the number and nature of their organs of locomotion, and in habitat. At the end of this chapter, we shall cite genera from these algal groups to illustrate important phenomena.

FORM AND ORGANIZATION IN ALGAE

The algae range from minute, simple types, as exemplified by one-celled species, to very large and complex ones (Figs. 2-1 and 2-5 through 2-9).

Unicellular, motile algae are grouped by some biologists along with unicellular, motile animals, in a separate kingdom (neither plant nor animal, but including attributes of both), namely, the *Protista*. Usually algal cells move by beating the water with one or more protoplasmic extensions called *cilia* or *flagella* (Figs. 2-2 and 2-8).

The green algae (Chlorophyta) have the most complete range of plant body type, for they include not only unicellular but also colonial, filamentous, and membranous genera. The association of organisms into groups of cells, or *colonies* (Fig. 2-1B, C), probably originated, as cohesion does in

---

* Genera (singular, *genus*): one of the categories of classification (each of which is a *taxon*) prescribed by the International Code of Botanical Nomenclature. This Code recognizes the following taxa in ascending order: *species, genus, family, order, class,* and *division*. In illustration of these, the alga, *Chlamydomonas eugametos,* is classified as follows:

    Division: Chlorophyta
      Class: Chlorophyceae
        Order: Volvocales
          Family: Chlamydomonadaceae
            Genus: *Chlamydomonas*
              Species: *Chlamydomonas eugametos*
It is conventional to italicize the generic and specific names in print.

Table 2-1

SUMMARY OF ALGAL DIVISIONS AND THEIR NOTEWORTHY ATTRIBUTES

Division	Common Name	Pigments	Stored Photosynthate	Cell Wall	Flagellar Number and Insertion [a]	Habitat
CHLOROPHYTA	green algae	Chloro.[b]a,b	starch	cellulose	2–8, equal, apical	f.w., b.w., s.w.,[c] t.
CHAROPHYTA	stoneworts	Chloro.a,b	starch	cellulose plus pectin	2, equal, apical	f.w., b.w.
EUGLENOPHYTA	euglenoids	Chloro.a,b	paramylon	absent	1–3, apical sub-apical	f.w., b.w., s.w.
CHRYSOPHYTA	golden algae (including diatoms)	Chloro.a, some have c, e, in some	oil, leucosin	pectin plus silicon dioxide	1–2, unequal or equal, apical	f.w., b.w., s.w., t.
PHAEOPHYTA	brown algae	Chloro.a,c	mannitol, laminarin	cellulose plus algin	2, unequal, lateral	f.w. (rare), b.w., s.w.
PYRROPHYTA	dinoflagellates, in part	Chloro.a,c	starch	cellulose or absent	2, 1 trailing, 1 girdling	f.w., b.w., s.w.
RHODOPHYTA	red algae	Chloro.a,d Phycocyanin, Phycoerythrin	floridean [d] starch	cellulose	absent	f.w. (some) b.w., s.w. (most)
CYANOPHYTA	blue-green algae	Chloro.a, Phycocyanin, Phycoerythrin	cyanophycean starch [e]	cellulose plus pectin	absent	f.w., b.w., s.w., t.

[a] In motile cells, when these are produced.
[b] Chloro. = Chlorophyll.
[c] f.w. = fresh water; b.w. = brackish water; s.w. = salt water; t. = terrestrial.
[d] Stains wine-red with iodine.
[e] Glycogen-like.

ontogeny (development of the individual), by the failure of the cells to separate after cell division. These associations are often so loose that a colony may be shaken apart into fragments, even individual cells. In some instances, however (in certain species of *Volvox,* for example, Fig. 2-1B), the individual cells of the colony are bound together by connections very much like the protoplasmic threads that pass through the cell membranes of higher organisms.* The repeated division of a single cell and its descendants in the same direction without separation of the cells produces a *filament,* which may be branched or unbranched (Fig. 2-1D, E, F). Algae may also be composed of sheets of cells, one or more layers thick; these are membranous or leaf-like (Figs. 2-1G and 2-6A). Certain green and yellow-green algae are composed of solitary or interwoven tubes. The latter are

* The significance of these connections is often cited in discussions dealing with organization. Do multicellular organisms and their complex activities represent merely the total of the activities of the individual cells of which they are composed? The presence of intercellular connections in multicellular organisms is interpreted by some biologists as evidence that there is supracellular unity and that the organism is the unit. Multinucleate, nonseptate organisms like *Rhizopus,* the black mold (Fig. 3-10A–D), support this view. Furthermore, electron microscopy has demonstrated that protoplasmic continuity through nonliving walls is even more extensive than had been observed with the light microscope.

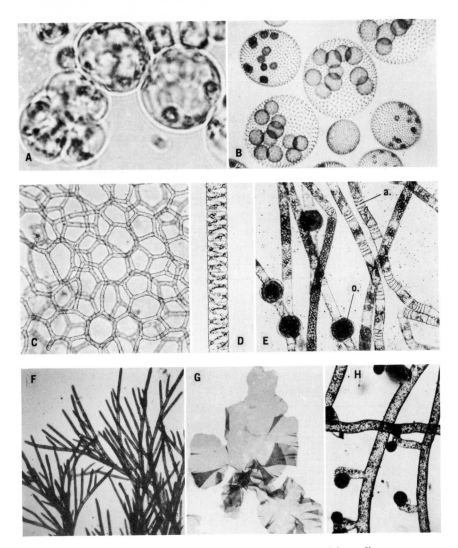

Fig. 2-1. Some genera of algae. (A) Chlorella, a unicellular form used in studies of photosynthesis; (B) Volvox, a spherical motile colonial alga; dark bodies are daughter colonies; (C) Hydrodictyon, "the water net," a nonmotile colonial alga; (D) Spirogyra, a filamentous alga; (E) Oedogonium, a filamentous alga showing sex organs, oogonia with eggs (o.), and antheridia (a.), each of which contains 2 sperms; (F) Cladophora, a branching filamentous alga; (G) Ulva, the "sea lettuce," a marine alga; (H) Vaucheria, a tubular alga without cross walls. (All but H are Chlorophyta or green algae; H is a yellow-green alga, Chrysophyta.)

not partitioned into individual cells (Fig. 2-1H). In complexity of external form and in size, the *kelps* (Fig. 2-6A) of the brown algae (*Phaeophyta*) probably are unsurpassed by other algae. Some of these enormous marine plants, which thrive in the cold waters off the American Pacific coast, and elsewhere, exceed 100 feet in length. The presence of phloem-like cells in kelps suggests the more complex land plants.

Algae differ in growth patterns, too. Growth in such algae as *Oscillatoria, Spirogyra,* and the sea lettuce, *Ulva,* for example, is generalized because increase in cell number and size is not confined to a specific region of the plant. In contrast, growth in other algae (*Fucus, Cladophora,* etc.) and all land plants is localized, usually at the apexes.

CELLULAR ORGANIZATION

With the exception of blue-green algae (Cyanophyta) (Fig. 2-4), cellular structure in algae does not differ fundamentally from that in other plants (Fig. 1-1), although there are variations in detail among the several groups. Pigmented bodies, the *chloroplasts* (Fig. 2-2A), are conspicuous organs of algal cells. These vary in form and pigmentation in the diverse genera and classes of algae (Table 2-1). The algal nucleus, however, is usually not conspicuous because it is often concealed by the more prominent plastids.

Motile algal cells, which may or may not be walled, have one or more flagella and may possess a *stigma,* or "red eye spot" (Figs. 2-2 and 2-8). The spot may be the site of light perception, and recent work has demonstrated that the wave lengths absorbed by the eye-spot pigment coincide with those that stimulate changes in the organism's orientation to light. *Contractile vacuoles,* like those that are present in protozoa, occur in the motile cells of many algae (Fig. 2-2).

As mentioned above, Cyanophyta differ in their cellular organization from all other algae (Fig. 2-4), being in some respects more like bacteria (Chapter 3) than algae. Their nuclear material, deoxyribose nucleic acid (DNA), is not partially delimited from the cytoplasm, as it is in other plants, by a readily demonstrable membrane; nucleoli and mitochondria are absent; the pigmented areas of the cytoplasm are organized differently from those of other algae in their lack of membranes enclosing plastids; finally, large watery vacuoles are absent from the cells.

REPRODUCTION IN ALGAE

When a unicellular alga divides, multiplication results, as it does at cell division in other unicellular organisms (Figs. 2-2B, C and 2-5A). Colonies and filaments may fragment, the several fragments subsequently developing into new organisms. Algae may also produce several types of specialized reproductive cells, among them motile *zoospores* and several types of nonmotile spores. All these methods of increasing the number of individuals in the population are nonsexual, or *asexual,* for they do not involve cell and nuclear union.

With the exception of only two groups (Cyanophyta and Euglenophyta), sexual processes are also widespread in algal reproduction. Since the unicellular alga *Chlamydomonas* is especially favorable for the study of sexuality, we shall consider the reproductive process in that organism in some detail.

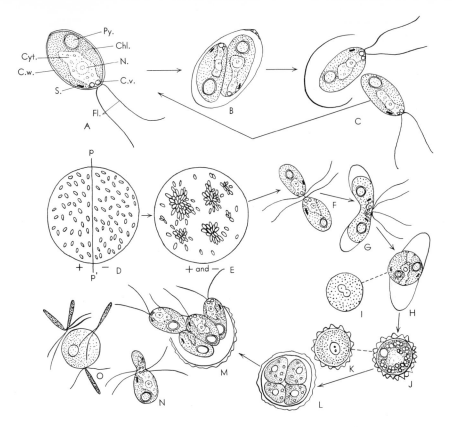

Fig. 2-2. The structure and reproduction of Chlamydomonas moewusii. **(A) Single individual (C.v., contractile vacuole; C.w., cell wall; Chl., chloroplast; Cyt., colorless cytoplasm; Fl., flagellum; N., nucleus; Py., pyrenoid; S., stigma). (B,C) Asexual reproduction; (D–O) Sexual reproduction: (D) + and − mating types separated along p-p′; (E) Clump formation after mating types are mixed; (F–H) Gamete pairing and union; (I) Union of gamete nuclei; (J,K) Zygotes, diploid nucleus visible at K; (L,M) Zygote germination after meiosis; (N)** Chlamydomonas sp., **heterogamy; (O)** Chlamydomonas sp., oogamy.

Chlamydomonas (Figs. 2-2 and 2-3) is a motile member of the Chlorophyta. In populations of *Chlamydomonas* where sexually mature and compatible individuals are present,* the sexual process begins with the clumping of individuals (Figs. 2-2E and 2-3B), which apparently are attracted to each other by chemical substances diffusing from their flagella. From these clumps, paired individuals emerge (Figs. 2-2F through H and 2-3C). In some species, the pair is connected by a cytoplasmic strand and is actively propelled by the two flagella of one member of the pair; in others, the uniting cells are not actively motile. As the process continues, the deli-

---

* When sexually compatible individuals are present in a culture that has arisen by asexual reproduction from one individual (a *clonal culture*), an organism is said to be *homothallic* or *bisexual;* where the compatible mating types are segregated in different clonal cultures or individuals, the organism is said to be *heterothallic,* each individual, or clone, being unisexual.

cate cell walls are dissolved at the point where the two cells are closest together, and the contents of the two cells flow together, producing a zygote (Figs. 2-2J, K, and 2-3D). Cells that unite in sexual reproduction are called *gametes*. Sooner or later, the two nuclei brought together in the zygote unite. This, of course, results in an association of two sets of parental chromosomes and their genes within a single nucleus. In the process just described for *Chlamydomonas,* several phenomena are present which characterize almost all sexual reproduction. These are: (1) the union of cells, (2) the union of nuclei, and (3) the association of chromosomes and genes. The parental chromosomes, however, retain their identity and do not unite in the fusion nucleus.

In *Chlamydomonas,* the uniting gametes are the young organisms themselves. In multicellular organisms, by contrast, the gametes are special cells of mature organisms formed for the specific function of reproduction.

Several other features of the sexual process in *Chlamydomonas* illustrate important biological principles. Although a number of organisms produce gametes that are *apparently* indistinguishable as "male" and "female," thus *isogamous* (Fig. 2-2F to H and 2-3), other species of *Chlamydomonas* and of most other organisms produce gametes that are clearly distinct from each other (Fig. 2-2N, O). Such gametes are called *heterogamous,* or *oogamous* if the larger one lacks flagella.

Among the algae (and other members of the plant and animal kingdoms), the development of the zygote may follow one of two paths (see chart p. 15): (1) the parental chromo-

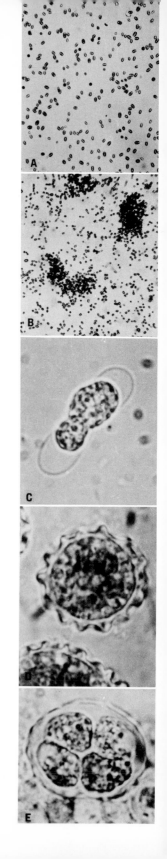

Fig. 2-3. The sexual reproduction of Chlamydomonas moewusii. **(A) Sexually mature cells of one mating type (−) alone; (B) The same shortly after adding + gametes— note clumps of gametes and free pairs; (C) Uniting gametes, enlarged (flagella not shown); (D) Dormant zygote; (E) Germinating zygote showing the 4 cells produced after meiosis. (Compare with Fig. 2-2.)**

somes and genes, brought together in the zygote nucleus, may segregate by *meiosis*,* a special type of nuclear division. In this process, the chromosome number is reduced by one-half and genic segregation occurs (life cycle A); or (2) the chromosomes may remain associated, each set then duplicating itself in nuclear divisions, *mitoses*.* In mitosis, the original chromosome number is preserved by reduplication, and genic segregation does not occur.

In the first alternative—(1) above and Type A, below—four *haploid* (n) cells † arise as a result of meiosis. This occurs in *Chlamydomonas* and certain other algae and fungi. But when the zygote nucleus undergoes mitotic, rather than meiotic, divisions, nuclei result with twice the chromosome and gene complement of the gametes; such nuclei are called diploid ($2n$) [(2), above and B and C, below]. This second alternative (mitotic rather than meiotic divisions of the zygote nucleus) occurs almost universally in the animal kingdom, in certain algae and fungi, and in the more complex plants having sexual reproduction.

(3) In another type of life cycle, in which the zygote and its descendants also divide mitotically to form a diploid organism, meiosis, when it occurs, may give rise to *spores* (C) rather than to gametes (B). Each haploid spore develops into a haploid phase (a free-living plant or merely a tissue), which at maturity forms gametes. Life cycle C includes two alternating phases or individuals that differ in chromosome number and type of reproductive cell produced. Accordingly, three fundamental patterns of reproductive, or life, cycle occur among algae and, in fact, among all living organisms. These may be summarized as follows:

TYPES OF REPRODUCTIVE OR LIFE CYCLES IN LIVING ORGANISMS

A. Plant (n) ⟶ gametes (n) —sexual union→ zygote ($2n$) —meiosis—

B. Plant ($2n$) —meiosis→ gametes (n) —sexual union→ zygote ($2n$) —

C. Plant ($2n$) —meiosis→ spores (n) ⟶ plant (n) ⟶ gametes (n) —sexual union→ zygote ($2n$) ←

The origin of the sexual process is unknown, but the study of simple algae such as *Chlamydomonas* has provided certain clues. That sexual

* See in this series C. P. Swanson, *The Cell,* 2nd ed. (Englewood Cliffs, N. J.: Prentice-Hall, 1964).

† In some cases, one or more of the nuclear products of meiosis may disintegrate.

reproduction is not necessary to maintain a race is clear from this fact: In certain organisms gametes that fail to unite may develop into new (haploid) individuals; this is an example of *parthenogenesis*. Recent researches indicate that although the sexual process (in plants) is a manifestation of profound physiological changes within organisms, it may be evoked or modified by a manipulation of certain external factors such as duration of illumination, temperature, and the amount of nitrogen available. It is clear also that the sexual process is the basic mechanism of evolution, for it affords the opportunity in all populations where it occurs to assemble new combinations of genes and to transmit them to subsequent generations. The importance of this process in bringing together two or more favorable mutant genes in one organism and its effect on survival and evolution can scarcely be overestimated. Conversely, the unfavorable combinations of genes that arise in sexual reproduction play a decisive role in the elimination of individuals and species in evolutionary competition.

NOTES ON SOME DIVISIONS OF ALGAE

In concluding this introduction to the algae, let us direct our attention again to their classification (Tables 1-1, 2-1). The major group of algae are blue-green algae (Cyanophyta), green algae (Chlorophyta), brown algae (Phaeophyta), and red algae (Rhodophyta). The remaining groups are smaller, yet they contain numerous economically important and biologically interesting organisms. We shall consider them one by one.

CYANOPHYTA. The blue-green algae take their name from the color of the cells of many of the species, although this color is by no means universal. In addition to the attributes cited in Table 2-1, blue-green algae, as we have seen, differ from other algae in their nuclear structure, organization of their pigmented cytoplasm, and absence of large, aqueous vacuoles and mitochondria (Fig. 2-4). In this respect

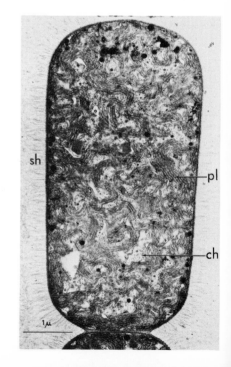

Fig. 2-4. Electron micrograph of the filamentous blue-green alga Anabaena sp. fixed with 1% osmium tetroxide. This median longitudinal section shows the contorted photosynthetic lamellae (pl) throughout the cell with interspersed chromatin areas (ch). The gelatinous sheath (sh) outside the cell wall appears as thin fibrils perpendicular to the wall with this fixation. × 14,433. (Courtesy Dr. Norma J. Lang)

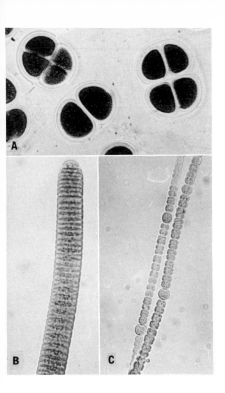

Fig. 2-5. Some representative blue-green algae (Cyanophyta). (A) Chroococcus, a unicellular form with cells just after division; (B) Oscillatoria and (C) Anabaena, filamentous genera.

and in the location of their DNA they are like bacteria. Blue-green algae are variously fresh-water, marine, terrestrial, or subterranean organisms, and often form conspicuous strata on the surface of moist rocks and soil. There are unicellular, colonial, and filamentous forms (Fig. 2-5). A few blue-green algae fix atmospheric nitrogen, like certain bacteria (see p. 24). A number live in and around hot springs where they color the surrounding rocks brilliantly. Sexual reproduction has not been observed in the blue-green algae.

CHLOROPHYTA. The green algae (Figs. 2-1 to 2-3) have many attributes in common with the more complex land plants, as is indicated by the data in Table 2-1. They are as widespread as blue-green algae, but are predominant in bodies of fresh water; many of the tubular forms, though, are marine. There are unicellular, colonial, filamentous, membranous, and tubular genera, and sexual reproduction can be either isogamous or oogamous. In addition, asexual reproduction by flagellate spores, which are called *zoospores,* occurs in a good many genera.

PHAEOPHYTA. The brown algae (Table 2-1, Fig. 2-6) are almost exclusively marine. The simplest among them are branching filaments; unicellular and colonial types are unknown. In this group also occur coarse plants like the *kelps* (Fig. 2-6A) and *rockweeds,* such as *Fucus* (Fig. 2-6B). The size and complexity of organization of the kelps exceed those of other algae and, indeed, those of many land plants.

RHODOPHYTA. The red algae (Table 2-1, Fig. 2-7) are also largely marine, although a number of fresh-water forms occur. Some of the red algae are particularly beautiful when mounted as herbarium specimens on white paper. In a number of red algae, the sexual reproductive process is quite complicated, and in the more complex types, three sequential phases occur in the reproductive cycle, namely: (1) a haploid sexual phase, (2) a diploid- and (3) a haploid spore-producing phase.

EUGLENOPHYTA. These plants (Table 2-1, Fig. 2-8), which are unicellular and flagellate, are well known through such examples as *Euglena, Phacus,* and *Trachelomonas.* These organisms may possess such animal-like attributes as contractile fibers at the cell surface, invaginations of

17

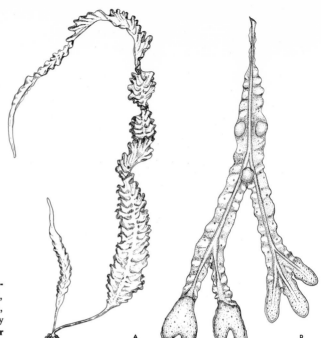

Fig. 2-6. Brown algae (Phaeo-phyta). (A) Laminaria agardhii, **a kelp; (B)** Fucus vesiculosus, **rockweed. (Bold,** Morphology of Plants, **New York: Harper & Brothers, 1957.)**

A

B

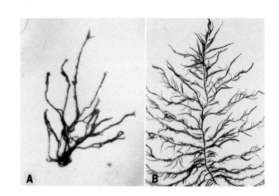

Fig. 2-7. Some representative red algae (Rhodophyta). (A) Nemalion, **a branched, worm-like genus; (B)** Dasya, **a branched, filamentous genus.**

A

B

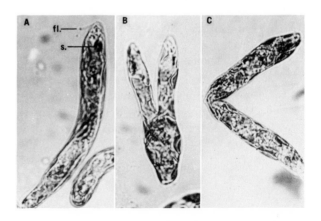

Fig. 2-8. Euglena mesnilii, **a unicellular organism. (A) Liv-ing individual, short flagellum, fl., and stigma, s., visible; (B), (C) Stages in reproduction by cell division, here binary fis-sion.**

A

fl.

s.

B

C

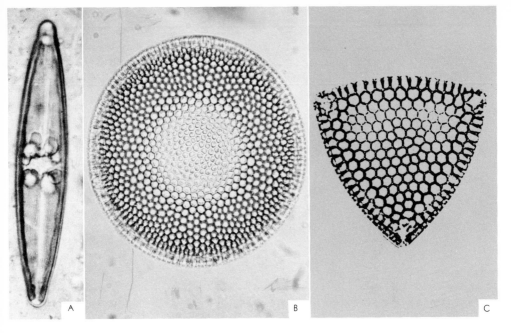

Fig. 2-9. Chrysophyta: diatoms. (A) Navicula **sp.;** (B) Coscinodiscus **sp.;** (C) Triceratium **sp.**

the cell surface, contractile vacuoles, and change of cellular form. Although their pigments are identical with those of Chlorophyta (Table 2-1), Euglenophyta differ from Chlorophyta in the nature of their storage products, their lack of cellulose walls, and in other details of cellular organization. Again, sexual reproduction is unknown in this group.

Finally, among the minor groups of algae, the diatoms (*Bacillariophyceae,* Table 2-1, Fig. 2-9) are organisms of great biological interest and economic importance; some of their significant features have already been cited. The cell walls of the numerous genera are impregnated with varying amounts of silicon dioxide. These walls (frustules) persist after the death of the protoplasts within, and vast deposits of them from ancient seas today furnish us with diatomaceous earth. The cells of certain diatoms are motile, but the mechanism of their motion is not entirely clear, since they lack flagella.

It is hoped that these pages have given you some insight into what algae are and how useful they are economically and biologically. The reference works listed under Selected Readings at the back of the book contain more complete accounts of these exceedingly important and interesting members of the plant kingdom.

Bacteria, Slime Molds, and Fungi

CHAPTER THREE

Chlorophyll-bearing plants, using light energy, are able to convert low-energy compounds—namely, carbon dioxide and water—into energy-rich carbohydrates in the process of photosynthesis. From simple sugars or fragments of them as basic units, with the addition of inorganic materials absorbed from the soil or the water in which they are bathed, green plants are able to synthesize their protoplasm. They are said to be *photoautotrophic,* therefore, because they use light energy to build living matter from inorganic substances. Of organisms lacking chlorophyll, the great majority are dependent on the complex substances manufactured by green plants for the materials with which to build their bodies; these organisms are *heterotrophic.* The distinction between these groups is not absolute. Certain green plants can live heterotrophically in light and darkness when supplied with appropriate organic compounds.

Some heterotrophic organisms, called *parasites,* require the living protoplasm of their hosts or grow upon them, sharing their metabolites.

Others are *saprophytic,* living upon nonliving protoplasm

or the nonliving products of protoplasm. They thus occur in soil and water containing organic matter and upon inadequately protected wood, textiles, and foods. The saprophytic heterotrophs are the main agents in degrading the complex products of other organisms and in causing decay of their bodies after death. They thus return to a common pool substances in many stages of breakdown to carbon dioxide, water, and many other inorganic compounds, which can be incorporated anew into the bodies of other organisms. These processes of degradation are especially striking as one digs down carefully through layers of undisturbed forest litter. Were it not for the activity of heterotrophs making available elements bound up in other organisms, life would be limited by a grave shortage of certain materials, especially available nitrogen.

A third group of heterotrophic organisms, which includes most animals, ingest protoplasm or its products; these are called *phagotrophic* or, sometimes, *holozoic.*

A few bacteria, although lacking chlorophyll, can synthesize their protoplasm from low-energy (inorganic) compounds by using the chemical energy released in oxidization of inorganic compounds (p. 23). Organisms of this type are said to be *chemoautotrophic.* It should be emphasized that the same essential major chemical elements (C, H, O, P, K, N, S, Ca, Fe, Mg) are present in the protoplasm of most living organisms. Differences, however, lie in the degree of complexity of carbon and nitrogen required for the synthesis of protoplasm. Autotrophic organisms start with simple compounds of these substances (CO_2, H_2O, NO_3, NH_3).

In the preceding paragraphs, we have, in effect, classified living organisms on the basis of their nutrition. With few exceptions, heterotrophic members of the plant kingdom comprise those organisms known as bacteria, slime molds, and fungi (Table 1-1). Most of these organisms are structurally as simple as or even simpler than the algae. It has been suggested by certain biologists that some of the fungi may have been derived from algae by loss of chlorophyll. Others consider protozoa as being ancestral to fungi, for some fungi, like protozoa, are phagotrophic.

Although united by their common lack of chlorophyll, and hence of photoautotrophic nutrition (excepting certain bacteria), considerable diversity exists among the bacteria, slime molds, and fungi, which, accordingly, are classified as separate groups (Table 1-1).

THE BACTERIA

Bacteria are probably the most simple and most minute living organisms with cellular organization. Bacterial cells are usually less than 8 microns * in length and may be as little as 0.5 micron in width. The cells of bacteria may be spheres, called *cocci* (singular, *coccus*), rods, called *bacilli,* or

---

* A micron (μ) is 0.001 mm or about 1/25,000 in.

twisted cells, called *spirilla* † (Fig. 3-1A–D). The first two may be joined to form colonies or filaments. The individual cells, like those of blue-green algae (p. 4), differ from other plants in their nuclear organization and lack of aqueous vacuoles (Fig. 3-1E). Bacterial cells contain DNA, the almost universal basis of heredity. Some genera have flagella (Fig. 3-1C,E) and, consequently, can move. Certain types form thick-walled spores (Fig. 3-1F,G) that are remarkably resistant to desiccation and unfavorable environmental conditions.

Bacteria multiply by cell division, which may be repeated rapidly, as often as once every 15–20 minutes. It has been estimated that if one bacterial cell continued to multiply at this rate for 24 hours, the number of individuals produced would be 1×10^{21}, with a weight of about 8,000 pounds! Why, then, is the world not overrun by bacteria? The answer, of course, is the specialized environment they require, the competition in

† There are *relatively* few directly observable morphological differences among the genera and species of bacteria. This has necessitated cultivating them in *axenic,* or *pure, cultures* and noting their attributes en masse. In pure cultures only one species of organism is present.

Fig. 3-1. Bacteria. (A) Cocci; (B) Bacilli, two in division; (C) Flagellated bacillus type; (D) Spirillum; (E) Cellular organization (Clifton, Introduction to Bacteria, New York: McGraw-Hill, 1958); (F) Spore formation; (G) Spore germination.

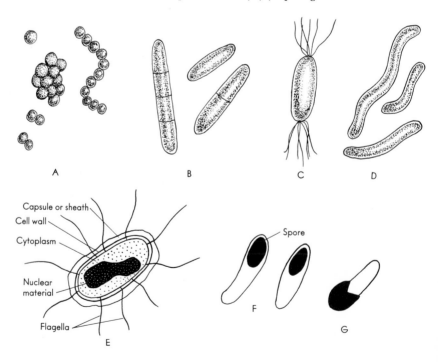

it with other microorganisms—namely, algae, other bacteria, protozoa, and fungi—and, finally, the accumulation of toxic products. Biologists sometimes lose sight of these facts in applying to natural situations conclusions based on pure cultures of microorganisms.

That certain bacteria also have a mechanism for genetic interchange was first demonstrated in 1947 by Dr. Joshua Lederberg when he cultivated together populations of two mutants of the colon bacillus *Escherichia coli;* each of the mutants was unable to synthesize two substances required in nutrition and metabolism. Out of each billion cells from the culture of mixed mutants planted in a medium lacking all four substances involved, approximately 100 colonies appeared. This is a clear manifestation that genetic interchange had occurred between individuals in the cultures of mixed mutants. These evidences of interchange of genes are incontrovertible, although the satisfactory demonstration of this change cytologically has been belated.*

That relatively simple morphology does not preclude physiological and biochemical complexity is strikingly evident in the bacteria. A few are chemo- and photoautotrophic in nutrition. The former obtain energy from oxidations to build their protoplasm from entirely inorganic units. Two nitrifying bacteria, *Nitrosomonas* and *Nitrobacter,* exemplify chemoautotrophic types; they obtain their energy as indicated below:

$$\textit{Nitrosomonas} \qquad NH_4^+ + 2O_2 \longrightarrow 2H_2O + NO_2^- \overset{+ \text{ energy}}{\uparrow}$$

$$\textit{Nitrobacter} \qquad NO_2^- + \tfrac{1}{2}O_2 \longrightarrow NO_3^- \overset{+ \text{ energy}}{\uparrow}$$

Photosynthetic bacteria, like *Rhodospirillum,* although photoautotrophic, carry on a type of photosynthesis quite different from that of plants that have chlorophyll *a,* for in these bacteria no free oxygen is released and hydrogen is provided by donor substances other than H_2O, with low expenditure of energy.

The vast majority of bacteria are heterotrophic, and their widespread chemical activities, catalyzed by myriads of enzymes, constitute the major areas of research in current microbiology and bacteriology. As they affect mankind, bacterial activities are both harmful and beneficial, but the beneficial ones probably exceed the harmful.

Bacteria cause disease in both plants and animals. These *pathogenic* types affect their hosts adversely by robbing them of vital metabolites, by enzymatically destroying the host tissues, and, sometimes, by secreting poisons. It is significant that some bacteria themselves are subject to the

* For another mechanism of interchange of genetic materials in bacteria see in this series D. M. Bonner and S. E. Mills, *Heredity,* 2nd ed. (Englewood Cliffs, N. J.: Prentice-Hall, 1964).

ravages of pathogens in the form of bacterial *viruses,* called *bacterio-phages,* which destroy the bacterial cell. Nonpathogenic bacteria can be bothersome too, for they are instrumental in spoiling foods and in causing decay in materials man desires to preserve.

The activities of bacteria in spoiling foods are only a special example of their universal activities in decay and degradation, processes accomplished by many types of bacteria and fungi through their enzymes. These processes culminate ultimately in the production of CO_2, H_2O, and many other inorganic compounds. The value of such destructive activities in freeing bound metabolites has already been cited (p. 21).

The importance of bacteria in maintaining soil fertility, especially with respect to the element nitrogen, which occurs in proteins, is paramount. Certain bacteria, either living freely in the soil or in the roots of legumes (beans, clover, alfalfa, etc.) use molecular nitrogen in synthesizing their protoplasm, thus tapping a source of nitrogen not available to most other organisms. (Several blue-green algae function similarly.) Other bacteria oxidize ammonia to nitrites and nitrates, and thereby enrich the nitrogen supply in the soil and reduce the escape of gaseous ammonia from soil.

The cheese industry depends on the bacteriological fermentation of lactose, a milk sugar, and the production from it of lactic acid, which coagulates the milk proteins, thus forming curds (and whey). The formation of acetic acid (in vinegar) is effectively accomplished by other bacteria; this occurs in the souring of cider and wines. Numerous other useful chemical activities of bacteria have been controlled for man's benefit.

Not the least important of these is the production, from bacteria, of mild *antibiotics* * such as tyrothricin, bacitracin, subtilin, polymyxin-B, and, from certain filamentous, bacteria-like organisms called actinomycetes, of powerful ones such as streptomycin, aureomycin, and terramycin. The latter are like fungi in having filaments and producing spores, but their nuclear and cellular organization and biochemical attributes link them more closely with bacteria.

Bacteria, like algae, are ancient organisms. They have been preserved as fossils, in spite of the delicacy of their cells, in Pre-Cambrian strata which are at least 620 million years old. Their manifold activities through the ages and at present emphasize their important role in the biological scheme. That they are classified as plants is largely because botanists made the early studies of bacteria. During the last 75 years, however, the study of bacteria has become a special area of biological science, *bacteriology.*

THE SLIME MOLDS (MYXOMYCETES)

The slime molds (Figs. 3-2 through 3-5) have been considered to be either "animal-like plants" or "plant-like animals," depending on whether

---

* Antibiotics are products of organisms (usually microorganisms) that arrest the development of one or more other organisms.

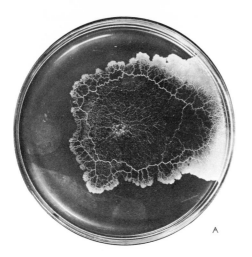
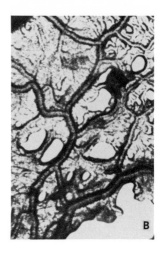

Fig. 3-2. (A) Plasmodium of Physarum polycephalum, a slime mold, on agar in a Petri dish (Courtesy C. J. Alexopoulos); (B) Portion of plasmodium magnified showing streams of unwalled protoplasm.

a botanist or a zoologist was involved. The modern biologist finds such questions of less critical interest, in view of the remarkable uniformity of organization and function of living systems at the molecular level, although the question has meaning from an evolutionary perspective. Since slime molds have been classified both as fungi and as protozoa, in this book we shall consider them as a division separate from other fungi (Table 1-1).

However classified, slime molds are inhabitants of soil and of many other habitats providing moist, decaying organic matter. In many of them two flagellate isogametes unite to produce a motile, diploid zygote (Fig. 3-4C,D). The latter sooner or later loses its flagella and becomes ameboid as it moves over the substratum, engulfing bacteria and organic particles which are digested in vacuoles. As this occurs, more protoplasm is synthesized, and the zygote nucleus divides mitotically. Repeated nuclear divisions of

Fig. 3-3. Spore-bearing structures of slime molds. (A) Diachea; (B) Lamproderma.

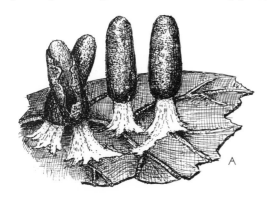
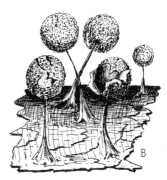

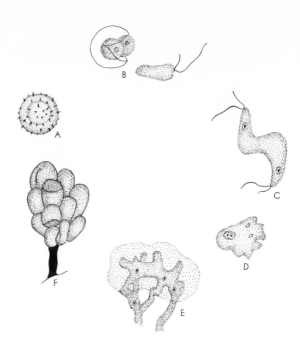

Fig. 3-4. Life cycle of a slime mold. (A) Dormant spore; (B) Spore germination to form motile gametes; (C) Gamete union; (D) Zygote; (E) Portion of plasmodium (compare with Fig. 3-2); (F) Sporangium. (Modified from Alexopoulos, courtesy John Wiley & Sons, Inc.)

the resulting diploid nuclei without cytoplasmic division result in the development of a more or less extensive ameboid mass of protoplasm, the *plasmodium* (Figs. 3-2 and 3-4E). This is considered to be the *somatic* (*vegetative*) phase of the life cycle.

Under suitable conditions of illumination, moisture, and nutrition, plasmodia several square feet in extent may arise. Sooner or later, localized upwellings of the plasmodium, with simultaneous dehydration, give rise again to a reproductive phase, the spore-producing one (Figs. 3-3 and 3-4F); this varies in form in the different genera of slime molds. As these spore-bearing structures mature, their nuclei undergo meiosis, and the spores (Fig. 3-4A), which arise by protoplasmic divisions, contain haploid nuclei. Upon dissemination, these spores germinate (on a suitably moist substrate) to form motile, flagellate gametes (Fig. 3-4B). The stationary, sporogenous phase, in contrast with the plasmodial one, is more typically plant-like. The naked, multinucleate plasmodia of slime molds, which can readily be maintained and increased in the laboratory, have long been favorite experimental material of biochemists and biophysicists, because plasmodia are available for immediate chemical analysis without the complication of nonliving cellulose walls, and they are excellent for the study of stimulus, response, and protoplasmic syntheses.

Superficially similar to Myxomycetes are the cellular slime molds, exemplified by *Dictyostelium* (Fig. 3-5), which has been a frequent and fruitful subject of biological investigation. Although they apparently have the same type of life cycle, they differ in forming a *pseudoplasmodium,* a mass of individual, uninucleate amebae that have aggregated after leading an individual existence. This group of aggregated amebae, called the

27

BACTERIA, SLIME MOLDS, AND FUNGI

"slug," also builds a spore-producing structure composed of amebae, some of which now function as spores (Fig. 3-5A). In the ontogeny of these organisms occurs the formation of a cell republic postulated by certain adherents of the cell theory. In summary, the pseudoplasmodium is preceded by a nutritive phase in which individual amebae feed and multiply independently. Later, when they gather together to form pseudoplasmodia and, finally, spores, they abandon their completely independent existence.

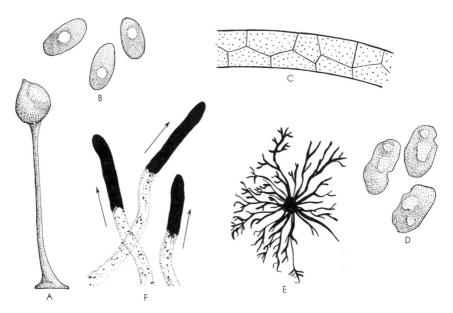

Fig. 3-5. Dictyostelium. (A) Stalked spore-bearing structure; (B) Spores; (C) Portion of stalk of A showing component cells; (D) Ameboid stage; (E) Streams of aggregating amebae; (F) Migrating pseudoplasmodia, or slugs, with slime trails behind. (Courtesy J. T. Bonner, Kenneth B. Raper, and the Princeton University Press.)

THE FUNGI

General Features

Fungi differ from the slime molds in lacking plasmodial stages and phagotrophic nutrition and from the bacteria in their nuclear organization; in this latter respect they are more like algae * and higher plants. The plant bodies of fungi are among the simplest in the plant kingdom, being either unicellular or filamentous. In the second type, the plant body is called the *mycelium;* the individual filaments are called *hyphae*. These may be composed of cells with one, two, or many nuclei; or they may be tubular,

* Other than blue-green algae.

with no transverse walls. The cell walls of most fungi are composed of chitin; others contain cellulose and other polysaccharides. The mycelium spreads over and through the substratum absorbing nutrients for growth. Fungi do this by secreting enzymes that digest some of the components of the substratum, the soluble products diffusing into the hyphae. Some fungi develop special absorptive branches, called *rhizoids* in saprophytic species and *haustoria* in parasitic species. In many fungi, the spore-producing filaments are raised above the remainder of the mycelium (Fig. 3-10).

Aquatic fungi with zoospores are considered primitive and the non-aquatic types with air-borne spores are presumed to have arisen from them. Both saprophytic and parasitic organisms occur. The type of parasitism varies from superficial and facultative to systemic and obligate.

In striking contrast with the relatively simple and unspectacular vegetative mycelium is the "fruiting" body which arises in some of the sac and club fungi (Fig. 3-6)—including the familiar morels, mushrooms (toadstools), puffballs, and shelf fungi. It it important to remember, however, that the fruiting body of a fungus has been preceded by an extensive vegetative mycelium which has grown sometimes for months or years.

Classification

The fungi include three groups, the *Phycomycetes* (algal fungi), *Ascomycetes* (sac fungi), and *Basidiomycetes* (club fungi); in addition two specialized groups are usually classified with them, namely, the Fungi Imperfecti and the lichens (Table 1-1). The Fungi Imperfecti have asexual spores and vegetative mycelium that suggest Ascomycetes or Basidiomycetes. Their failure to produce the typical ascospores or basidiospores of those groups and to manifest any sexual reproduction make their affinities doubtful, however; hence they are grouped separately. The lichens will be discussed below with the Ascomycetes.

PHYCOMYCETES. The Phycomycetes, or algal fungi, were so named by early students because they saw in the nonseptate mycelium of these fungi a similarity to the tubular organization of certain algae (Fig. 2-1H). Algal affinities for the group were further suggested by their aquatic habitat, by the zoospore production (Fig. 3-8B,C) of some of the genera, and by the gametes and gametangia (sex organs) in the sexual reproduction of others. The Phycomycetes include unicellular organisms, called chytrids, and mycelial types such as the aquatic water molds (Fig. 3-8) and black molds (Fig. 3-10A–D). A few are parasitic, causing economically important plant diseases such as grape and potato blights. One or more species are fatally parasitic to house flies.

ASCOMYCETES. The Ascomycetes include the simple yeasts (Fig. 3-7), the brown, green, and pink molds (Fig. 3-9 and 3-10 E–G), cup fungi (mostly saprophytic), and the parasitic powdery mildews. The *ascus* usu-

Fig. 3-6. Spore-bearing, "fruiting bodies" of fungi (A) Ascocarp of Peziza sp., a cup fungus; (B) Ascocarp of Morchella sp., a morel; (C) Nidularia sp., bird's nest fungus; (D) Psalliota campestris, edible mushroom; (E) Calvatia sp., a puff ball; (F) Polyporus sp., a shelf-like, pore fungus. (A and B, Ascomycetes; C–F, Basidiomycetes.)

ally contains four or eight *ascospores* (Fig. 3-10G). An ascus is a cell within which ascospores are formed, some cytoplasm not being incorporated within the spores. The asci may be formed directly or in a special fruiting body, the *ascocarp* (Figs. 3-6A, B and 3-10G).

Lichens (Fig. 3-11) are organisms composed of an alga (green or blue-green) and a fungus. They are classified with Ascomycetes or Basidiomycetes, depending on their fungus component. The nutritive relations between the components have inspired much uncritical speculation, and the real relationships are only now being investigated by the techniques of pure culture. Recent work has shown that both the algal and fungal components of a lichen may lead independent existences in the same culture medium, even when placed in contact. Only when nutrition is minimal or subminimal is the intimate association of fungus and alga re-established to form a lichen.

BASIDIOMYCETES. To the Basidiomycetes belong those fungi that produce *basidia* and *basidiospores* freely on the mycelium or in *basidiocarps* (Figs. 3-6C–F and 3-13A,B). *Basidia* are either club-like hyphae, each with (usually) the four *basidiospores* borne at its apex (Fig. 3-13C), or septate hyphae arising upon germination of thick-walled spores (Fig. 3-12F[b]). The Basidiomycetes include the economically important parasitic *rusts* and *smuts* of cereal grains and other plants, the pored *shelf* fungi, some of which destroy timber and lumber, and the puffballs and mushrooms (Figs. 3-6C through F and 3-13).

Illustrative Types of Fungi

From the vast assemblage of fungi, we can only give detailed consideration to a few examples, those that illustrate certain biological principles. Among the simplest fungi is the group known as yeasts, exemplified by the brewer's yeast, *Saccharomyces cerevisiae*. Yeasts, which occur commonly in nature on ripening fruits, are simple unicellular organisms (Fig. 3-7). Cellular multiplication by an unequal bipartition known as *budding* rapidly increases the population in suitable environments containing sugar.

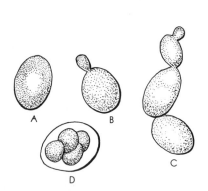

Fig. 3-7. Saccharomyces cere-visiae, **brewer's yeast, highly magnified. (A–C) Reproduction by budding; (D) Ascus containing ascospores.**

That *Saccharomyces* is an ascomycete is apparent by its production under certain conditions of ascospores in groups of four (Fig. 3-7D). The yeast plant, of course, has been the servant of mankind from antiquity, both as a leavening agent and as a producer of ethyl alcohol from sugars. This degradation of sugar, known as *fermentation,* is catalyzed by an enzyme complex called *zymase,* is intracellular, and is enhanced under anaerobic conditions. The low energy yield is evidence of the incomplete breakdown of sugar; much more energy still remains in the alcohol produced. Some yeast-like fungi are pathogenic and parasitize human beings.

The remaining types of fungi to be discussed are mycelial, hence multicellular. *Achlya* (Fig. 3-8), a phycomycete, one of the "water molds," is an organism whose numerous species may be isolated readily from pond water and soil submerged in water. The substrate in nature is often a dead insect, but in the laboratory, boiled, split hemp seeds and other small seeds are favorite "bait." Most species of *Achlya* are saprophytic, but parasitism—on fish, for example—occurs in the related genus *Saprolegnia.* The mycelium of *Achlya* forms a radiating mass of branching, tubular,

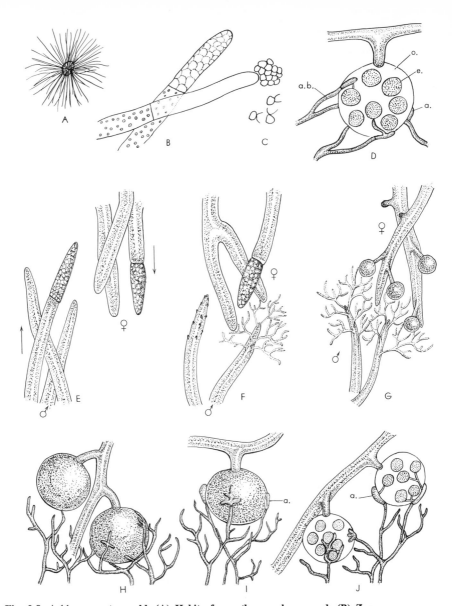

Fig. 3-8. Achlya, a water mold. (A) Habit of growth on a hemp seed; (B) Zoosporangia, with one shedding its spores; (C) Zoospores; (D) Sex organs, oogonium, o., containing eggs, e., appressed antheridial branches, a.b., and antheridia, a.; male nuclei from the antheridia are transported by tubes to the eggs; (E–J) Hormonal control of sexual maturation in Achyla; (E) Male and female branches growing close; both have only asexual zoosporangia; (F) Proximity causes proliferation of hyphae of ♂ to form slender antheridial hyphae; (G) The formation of antheridial hyphae stimulates the ♀ mycelium to form oogonial branches; (H,I) Formation of these branches causes growth of antheridial hyphae directly toward the oogonia; upon making contact, the antheridial hyphae branch, and their tips are cut off as antheridia, a.; (J) Contact of the antheridial hyphae and antheridia with the oogonium stimulates cleavage of the latter into eggs and fertilization occurs. Each of the stages from E to J is brought about by the secretion and diffusion of sexually active substances, sometimes called sex hormones. (After J. Raper, courtesy American Scientist, January, 1951.)

multinucleate, nonseptate filaments surrounding the substrate (Fig. 3-8A), an evidence of the efficiency of the absorptive rhizoids and their enzymes within. After a short period of development, the tips of certain hyphae are delimited by septa and function as zoosporangia (Fig. 3-8B), each of which produces a large number of biflagellate zoospores. After a period of rest at the mouth of the sporangium, zoospores migrate to other available substrata and form new mycelia and zoosporangia. Apparently because growth depletes certain substances, sexual reproduction is initiated. Particularly interesting investigations have been made of this process as it occurs in the species *Achlya ambisexualis*. In this organism, in which the male and female sex organs (Fig. 3-8D) are produced on separate individuals (heterothallism), the formation and functioning of the sex organs are controlled by chemical substances from the sterile male and female plants and later from their differentiated sexual branches themselves. The rather complex process is summarized in Fig. 3-8E through J, which illustrates the orderly, progressive, and correlated steps in the production of sex organs. The chemicals that evoke these steps are termed *hormones*.

Fig. 3-9. Culture of a blue-green mold, Penicillium, growing on potato-dextrose agar in a Petri dish.

Several genera of molds (Figs. 3-9 and 3-10) are significant for a variety of reasons. Among these are *Rhizopus stolonifer*, called "black mold of bread," a phycomycete, and *Aspergillus* and *Penicillium*, both of which have ascomycetous affinities. Most of these genera are saprophytic and widespread on organic substrate; their air-borne spores are everywhere. Flagellate motile cells do not occur in the life cycles of these fungi. A piece of moistened bread, exposed to the atmosphere and then covered by a glass tumbler, often will support colonies of all these genera, several of which, indeed, are common agents of mildew upon bread.

In *Rhizopus* (Fig. 3-10A–D) the tubular, multinucleate hyphae are differentiated into prostrate branches, absorptive rhizoids, and erect *sporangiophores*. The blackness of the walls of the myriad spores is responsible for the color of the mature fungus. If the spores fall upon suitable substrata, they germinate and produce mature, sporebearing mycelia within

72 hours under favorable conditions. It was in *Rhizopus* that sexual repro-
duction of fungi was first demonstrated early in the present century. When
compatible mating types grow close together, the sexual process results
(Fig. 3-10D), and it, too, is clearly affected by hormone-like secretions.
Unless both mating types are present, only asexual reproduction occurs.
Meiosis is probably zygotic in *Rhizopus*.

Aspergilus and *Penicillium* (Figs. 3-9 and 3-10E through G) are brown
and blue-green molds, respectively. Here again, the color resides in the
spore walls, although certain species like *Penicillium chrysogenum* secrete
a golden-yellow pigment into the culture medium. The asexual spores are
borne in chains on erect branches of the mycelium (Fig. 3-10E,F). Some
species produce closed ascocarps, and asci and ascospores (Fig. 3-10G),
presumably after sexual fusions. *Penicillium* is an especially important

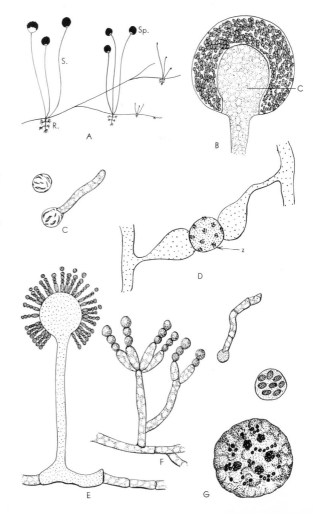

Fig. 3-10. Molds. (A–D) Rhizopus stolonifer, "black mold
of bread": (A) Habit of growth
(R., absorptive rhizoids; S.,
sporangiophores; Sp., sporangia); (B) Median longitudinal
section of sporangium with
sterile, central columella C.,
covered by spores; (C) Spore
germination; (D) Sexual stage
with zygote, z.; (E) Aspergillus, a brown mold, with
globose spore-bearing head;
(F) Penicillium, a broom-like
blue-green mold with chains of
spores, one germinating below
D; (G) Section of ascocarp of
Penicillium, one ascus with
ascospores enlarged, above.

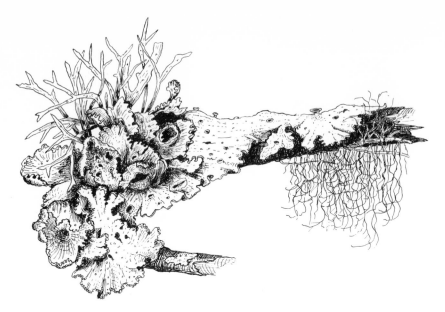

Fig. 3-11. Lichens: several species on an oak branch; the fibrous, pendulous form at the right is a species of *Usnea* called "the old man's beard."

genus, since it affects human welfare in several ways. On the adverse side, certain species may cause respiratory infections, mildewing of clothing, and food spoilage, especially of citrus fruits and apples. Other species, though, have important roles in the manufacture of such cheeses as Roquefort and Camembert. Far overshadowing all other useful activities, however, is the production of the lifesaving antibiotic *penicillin* by *Penicillium chrysogenum.*

Neurospora, a pink ascomycetous mold, has contributed heavily to our knowledge of the mechanisms of heredity and gene action; for more on this matter, see in this series *Heredity* by David Bonner.

Among the Basidiomycetes, the *rusts* are worth consideration for two reasons: economically, as the causes of decreased yields in grains and other plants, and biologically as classic examples of several striking phenomena. The wheat rust, a strain of *Puccinia graminis,* grows parasitically in the leaves and stems of wheat (other races occur on other grains), absorbing materials from the wheat protoplasm. At maturity, the hyphae of *P. graminis* erupt as localized lesions on the host leaves and stems, producing large numbers of rust-colored spores that repeat the cycle, thus infecting many new plants. At least four additional types of reproductive cells are produced in the life cycle of this fungus (Fig. 3-12). A number of features of the wheat rust are significant. *Puccinia graminis* is an *obligate parasite,* that is, it has never been cultivated apart from its wheat host,* or the

* A related rust fungus parasitizing cedar trees has recently been cultivated apart from its host.

alternate host. Apparently, the hosts alone can supply it, during most of its life cycle, with the substances it requires to build its protoplasm. How were this and similar host-parasite relationships initiated in the course of evolution? This specific requirement of *P. graminis tritici* for wheat protoplasm is the more remarkable because in another phase of its life cycle (Fig. 3-12H), the parasite is dependent on another host plant, the native American barberry, *Berberis vulgaris,* which is not closely related to wheat.

In bringing this chapter to a close, let us devote our attention to mushrooms (Figs. 3-6D and 3-13), the inedible and poisonous species of which are called "toadstools" by the layman. The mushroom itself is the basidiocarp, or fruiting body, of the organism. It is organized and preceded by an extensive vegetative mycelium. The mushroom is unlike most plants and animals, in which cells divide and redivide to form the tissues of the body. The mushroom, in contrast, is built up by complicated interweavings of filamentous mycelium. The mushroom cap bears *gills* on its lower

Fig. 3-12. Life cycle of wheat rust, Puccinia graminis tritici. **(A) Portion of infected wheat plant. Black streaks contain urediniospores, as at (B). These germinate (C) and infect other wheat plants (D). Ultimately teliospores (E) are produced on the wheat plants. These thick-walled spores germinate after a period of dormancy (F) to form a septate basidium, b, from which four basiodiospores, ba., are explosively discharged; if these land on a barberry leaf, they infect it upon germination and form cuplike structures, aecia, full of spores (G); sections of the barberry leaf (H) show the aeciospores (below) and flask-like spermagonia, s. Aeciospores, upon germination (I), infect young wheat plants (J), and the cycle is thus completed.**

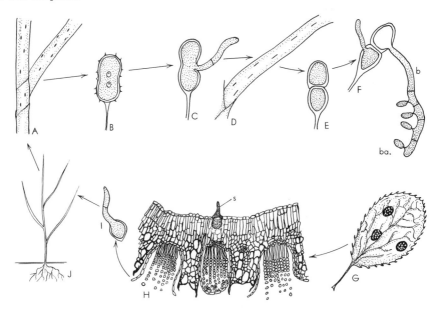

surface. The gills (Fig. 3-13A–C), themselves composed of interwoven hyphae, produce the basidia and basidiospores (Fig. 3-13). Meiosis occurs in the basidium so that the basidiospores are haploid (*n*). These, upon germination, initiate a *primary mycelium,* the cells of which are uninucleate. When compatible pairs of such mycelia are grown together, fusions (plasmogamy) occur between certain compatible cells, but nuclear union does not occur. This initiates the *secondary mycelium,* with binucleate (*n* + *n*) cells, which alone can form the basidiocarp. The common edible mushroom, *Psalliota* (*Agaricus*) *campestris,* is grown commercially from "spawn." This is a mass of soil, manure, and rotting leaves containing the mycelium of the fungus. When planted into properly prepared beds, the basidiocarps—that is, the mushrooms—develop after a period of vegetative growth of the mycelium.

Fig. 3-13. Life cycle of a mushroom. (A,B) Fruiting structures, or basidiocarp, showing gills; (C) Portion of a gill: (1) binucleate basidium; (2) basidium after nuclear fusion; (3) basidium after meiosis; (4) early stage in formation of basidiospores; (5) mature basidiospores. (D) Basidium and basidiospores enlarged; (E) Spore germination and formation of young mushroom. (a, b) Spores of two mating types germinating; the resulting primary mycelia coalesce (see arrow) and form secondary mycelium from which a new basidiocarp will arise. (1) and (1') are enlargements of primary mycelia containing nuclei of opposite mating type; (2) is an enlarged segment of secondary mycelium showing that compatible nuclei have been brought togther in the same mycelium; (ba.) initiation of basidiocarp. (F) Immature basidiocarp.

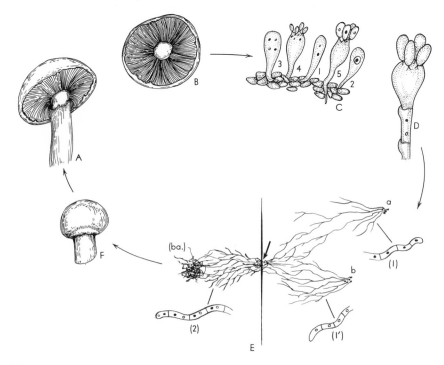

Two additional features of mushrooms are of special interest, namely, the bioluminescence of some species and the hallucinogenic properties of others. The mycelium of certain mushrooms, both in laboratory culture and in nature, is luminescent. This luminescence, it has been demonstrated, is mediated by the enzyme *luciferase* in the presence of *luciferin* as substrate. Substances bearing a similar name are also functional in the firefly, but evidence to date indicates they are there of a different chemical nature.

Psilocybe * *mexicana,* a mushroom, and related species were and are valued for the ecstatic effects they generate when eaten. The chemical nature of the active substances is being investigated, and one of the hallucinogenic substances synthesized is being used in the study of certain mental aberrations.

Finally, it is significant that in the majority of Basidiomycetes, although a sexual process occurs, differentiated organs of sexual reproduction are not developed. This is, perhaps, but one step beyond isogamous organisms, in which the gametes, although specially differentiated, are not morphologically distinguishable. These and related processes of lower plants are instructive with respect to the sexual process in general, because they are not obscured by secondary and supplementary phenomena. The fungi include a wealth of material for biological experimentation and, like the bacteria, are of fundamental importance in medicine, industry, and other aspects of human welfare.

* Pronounced *Sigh-lós-i-bee.*

Nonvascular Land Plants: Mosses and Liverworts

It is generally believed that life first arose in an aquatic environment and that terrestrial plants and animals are the descendants of aquatic ancestors. Accordingly, land plants are considered to be the modified progeny of algae. In the plants that now populate and have in the past populated the earth, two contrasting groups are apparent, one seemingly derived from haploid and the other from diploid algal ancestors. The plants of the first group, liverworts and mosses, are characterized by a lack of *vascular tissue,* that is, *xylem* and *phloem,* which are, respectively, water- and food-conducting tissues. The absence of vascular tissue probably accounts for the relatively small size of liverworts and mosses, since they do not have efficient systems for transporting water and food rapidly over any considerable distance. Plants in the second group have vascular tissue; this characteristic probably is correlated with the large size and complexity of many vascular plants and their ability to live in harsh terrestrial habitats. To this group belong the ferns and other seedless vascular plants as well as the seed-bearing plants.

Although liverworts and mosses are usually placed before

the vascular plants in classifications of the plant kingdom (Table 1-1), they are not more ancient, according to present evidence from the fossil record (Fig. 6-1). Their place in systems of classification is probably inspired by their relative simplicity of form, by their small size, and by the lack of evidence that they are related to the vascular plant.

MOSSES

Mosses are widespread in rainy and humid places, but are rare in more arid zones. Only a few species are adapted to survive a long drought, although many successfully withstand temporary desiccation. The individual moss plant (Figs. 4-1 and 4-2) consists of a slender leafy axis, either erect or prostrate, which may or may not have multicellular absorptive branches called rhizoids.* It is characteristic of mosses that they rarely occur as individuals but form extensive groups or colonies on moist soil, rocks, and wood. The largest mosses are natives of the Southern Hemisphere and may exceed a foot in length, but in the Northern Hemisphere the large species of the "hair-cap moss," *Polytrichum,* do not usually exceed 6 to 8 inches (Figs. 4-1 and 4-2). Mosses growing on soil are important in preventing erosion. The genus *Sphagnum* (Fig. 4-1A), known as "peat" or "bog" moss, is of commercial value in horticulture because of its capacity to hold water and to increase the acidity of soils even when it is dead and pulverized. It often invades bodies of water and forms extensive surface mats, or "quaking bogs."

It is convenient to begin consideration of the moss life cycle with the

* You should distinguish the terms "rhizoid," "rhizome," and "root." Rhizomes are elongate, fleshy, nonvertical stems often growing upon or under the surface of the soil. Rhizoids are root-like in performing the functions of anchorage and absorption. They lack root caps and xylem and phloem, which characterize roots.

Fig. 4-1. (A) Sphagnum; **portion of a clump of plants; (B)** Polytrichum; **female plants (♀) with maturing sporophytes (s.); (C)** Funaria; **female branches (♀) with developing sporophytes (s.); note peaked calyptras (c.).**

spore. Like other land plants, mosses produce air-borne spores that are usually able to withstand desiccation for long periods.* Moss spores are widely distributed in the atmosphere, and those that come to rest upon favorable, moist surfaces then absorb water and renew their growth in the process called germination. The spores of many mosses develop into prostrate filamentous systems that branch profusely. These filaments are often divided by slanting walls, and their cells are filled with disc-like chloroplasts. The system of branching filaments that develops from the germinating spore is known as the *protonema* (Fig. 4-3A,B). After a period of development, during which extensive surfaces may be covered, the protonema forms buds (Fig. 4-3B) which grow into leafy shoots (Fig. 4-3C). The protonema at the bases of these shoots serves as a rhizoidal system, but additional rhizoids develop on the leafy axes. Although moss leaves and stems may achieve considerable internal complexity, vascular tissues are absent, and water is absorbed directly through the surfaces of the leaves and stems in many genera. In most populations, the densely aggregated plants tenaciously hold considerable amounts of capillary water. A few mosses grow in annual cycles, but a majority have leafy shoots which persist for a number of growing seasons; such species are said to be *perennial*.

At certain times of the year, the tips of moss plants become fertile (Fig. 4-2), producing sex organs, or gametangia. As in all land

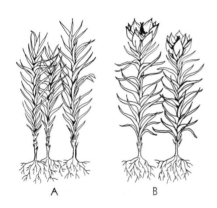

Fig. 4-2. Polytrichum **sp. (A) Three ♀, or female, and (B) two ♂, or male, plants.**

* Certain algal spores and zygotes and the spores of nonaquatic fungi also may be air-borne.

Fig. 4-3. Funaria. (A) One ungerminated and several germinating spores; (B) Portion of protonema (p.) with bud (b.) which will develop into leafy plant; (C) young leafy shoots attached to protonema.

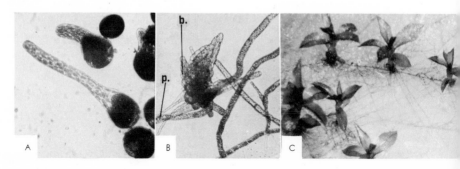

plants, reproduction is oogamous, the female gamete being a nonmotile *egg cell* and the male gamete, a *sperm*. The latter is small and motile, either flagellate or ameboid. The male gametangium, the *antheridium* (Fig. 4-4A), and the female gametangium, the *archegonium* (Fig. 4-4B), are multicellular, and their gametes are covered by a sterile cellular layer (unlike the gametangia of algae and fungi).

Some species of mosses are homothallic, both antheridia and archegonia being present on the same individual, while others, like *Polytrichum* (Fig. 4-2), are heterothallic. The fertile bisexual apexes of homothallic and the male apexes of heterothallic mosses are often recognizable because the leaves form a sort of cup about the sex organs (Fig. 4-2B).

During heavy dews or rainfall, mature antheridia discharge their sperm (Fig. 4-4C), some of which may reach the vicinity of an archegonium; in heterothallic species, the contact may be accomplished by means of splashing rain drops. The inner cells of the neck disintegrate when the archegonium is mature, leaving a liquid-filled passageway to the egg. It is suggested by studies of other organisms that substances secreted in the moss archegonium chemically attract sperm. When

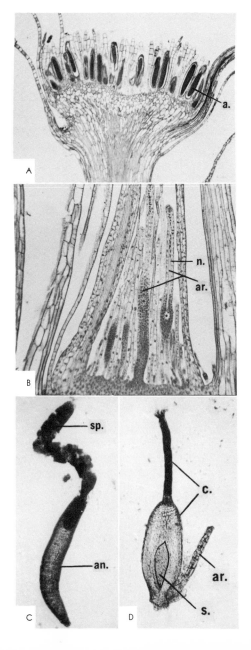

Fig. 4-4. (A) Mnium: **Median longitudinal section (m.l.s.) of apex of ♂ plant with numerous antheridia (a.) and sterile filaments among them; (B)** Mnium; **m.l.s. of apex of ♀ plant with archegonia (ar.) and interspersed sterile filaments and archegonial neck (n.); (C)** Funaria; **antheridium (an.) shedding sperms (sp.); (D)** Funaria: **Enlarging archegonium or calyptra (c.) containing young sporophyte (s.).**

a minute, biflagellate sperm, composed largely of nuclear material, swims down the canal of the archegonial neck, and enters the egg cell, nuclear union, or fertilization, follows, and a zygote is formed.

As in certain algae (see page 15) the moss zygote does not undergo meiosis, and it, too, gives rise to an alternate, spore-producing structure, the *sporophyte*. However, unlike the sporophyte of many algae, which are free-living, independent organisms, the moss sporophyte is retained permanently on the parent gametophyte and, during its early development, within the now enlarging archegonium (Fig. 4-4C). These circumstances no doubt have exerted a profound effect on the form of the moss sporophyte. Its incipient growth and nutrition certainly are based on metabolites from the archegonium (called the *calyptra* as it enlarges after fertilization) and the leafy axis, but very soon the cells of the developing sporophyte become chlorophyllous, an indication that it is at least partially photoautotrophic. Still, the nitrogen and other elements that come from the soil necessarily must diffuse into the sporophyte from the gametophyte, which, in turn, has absorbed them from the soil.

Development of the sporophyte from the zygote is very rapid in mosses, and the needle-like sporophyte appears above the apex of the leafy plant after it has ruptured the calyptra following fertilization.* Part of the calyptra is carried upward at the summit of the sporophyte (Figs. 4-1C and 4-5E). When the latter has reached the length characteristic of its species, its tip enlarges to form a spore-bearing region called the *capsule,* or *sporangium* (Figs. 4-1 and 4-5). The capsule is connected to the leafy gametophyte by a stalk, or *seta,* and a basal *foot,* the latter buried in the stem apex of the leafy shoot.

The moss capsule is quite complex and varies in structure among the numerous genera. It is significant that only a small fraction of the component tissues is sporogenous; the remaining tissues are photosynthetic and vegetative in function until late in development, when the surface layers thicken and become hard and brown. The cells of the sporogenous layers undergo meiosis in two successive nuclear and cell divisions. Each cell undergoing meiosis produces a group of four spores, called the tetrad. In all land plants, the cell undergoing meiosis to form a tetrad of spores is called a *sporocyte,* or *spore mother cell.*

The mechanisms of spore liberation and dissemination are a fascinating aspect of mosses and well worthy of study. In most mosses, the calyptra and capsule apex (the *operculum*), when shed after the spores have formed, reveal a structure known as the *peristome.* This is a single or double ring of tooth-like segments around the mouth of the capsule (Fig. 4-5D, 4-6). Two types of these are illustrated in Fig. 4-5D and H. Peristomal movements, which are triggered by slight changes in humidity, result in gradual

---

* Although the eggs of several archegonia at the tip of a single leafy shoot may be fertilized, usually only one zygote develops into a sporophyte.

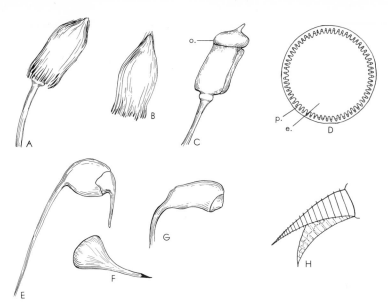

Fig. 4-5. Moss capsule structure. (A–D) Polytrichum: **(A) Capsule covered by calyptra; (B) Calyptra; (C) Capsule with calyptra removed showing operculum, o.; (D) Mouth of capsule with peristome teeth, p., and membranous epiphragm, e. (E–H)** Funaria; **(E) Capsule with calyptra; (F) Calyptra; (G) Capsule with calyptra removed showing operculum, o.; (H) Portion of outer (above) and inner peristome.**

and continuous spore dissemination under favorable (dry) conditions. Here is the life cycle of a typical moss:

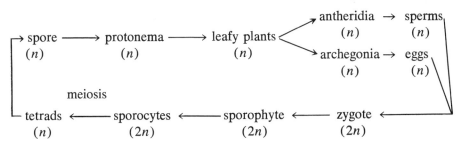

Mosses have not received adequate study by researchers because they seem to be difficult to grow to maturity in laboratory cultures. As a result, we are inadequately informed about their physiological processes and their growth and nutritional requirements. Polyploid * races of certain genera of mosses have been obtained by cutting up and planting pieces of setae on moist substrata or by wounding the base of the capsule. Since

* The term *polyploid* is used to designate an organism or phase (a nucleus, cell, or tissue, for example) that has a multiple of the basic number of chromosomes characteristic of the phase or organism. Thus, gametophytes normally are n and sporophytes $2n$ in chromosome constitution, but naturally occurring and experimentally produced gametophytes may have n, $2n$, or $3n$, etc. chromosomal constitutions. Similarly, sporophytes may be $2n$, $3n$, $4n$, etc.

these are diploid, they form diploid protonemata and, subsequently, diploid leafy shoots. The chromosome number (*n* or 2*n*) of itself does not determine whether cells are sporophytic or gametophytic. The diploid cells from the regenerating seta form a gametophytic protonema, not a sporophyte, even though they are diploid. This is but a small segment of the larger problem of how the genes effect differentiation in form and function.

One final point: The gametophytic and sporophytic phases of mosses and other plants should not be considered as two different, almost antagonistic, entities, for both are manifestations of the same organism in its complete reproductive cycle. This is strikingly illustrated by the remarkable regenerative capacity of mosses: Rhizoids, leaves, and stems and their fragments, the various parts of the sporophyte, and even the antheridia and

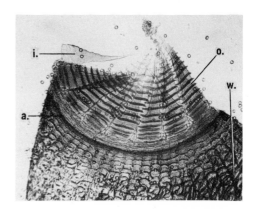

Fig. 4-6. Funaria; **portion of capsule wall and peristome, somewhat flattened; note spores (a., region of the annulus; i., inner peristome segment; o., outer peristome tooth; w., capsule or sporangium wall).**

archegonia * may regenerate new protonema and subsequent stages of the complete life cycle.

LIVERWORTS

Liverworts received their rather curious name long ago because the lobing of the plant bodies of some genera suggested an animal liver. Some botanists consider liverworts to be closely akin to the mosses and classify them together in the division Bryophyta; others have challenged this view (Table 1-1) because of differences in the organization of both the gametophytic and sporophytic phases. Liverworts, with few exceptions, seem to require moister conditions than do mosses (Fig. 4-7A,B). They grow on moist soil, rocks, and tree bark. The rhizoids of liverworts, in contrast to those of mosses, are unicellular. The liverwort sporophyte is less complex than that of mosses and lacks a peristome. The sporophyte of one genus,

* Formation of protonema from antheridia and archegonia has recently been demonstrated in the author's laboratory by Mr. James H. Monroe.

Fig. 4-7. Liverworts (Hepatophyta). (A) Riccia sp. **on soil; (B)** Leucolejeunea, a **leafy liverwort; (C)** Anthoceros sp., **"horned liverwort" with needlelike sporophytes (s.).**

the horned liverwort, *Anthoceros* (Fig. 4-7C), is remarkably complex and long-lived; its growth and spore production continue for several months. As in the mosses, the sexual gametophyte of liverworts is the free-living, dominant phase, and the sporophyte is always attached to it. Although most liverwort sporophytes, like those of mosses, are photosynthetic and presumably photoautotrophic, there is little experimental evidence to support this claim. The presence of sex chromosomes in plants was first clearly demonstrated in a liverwort, *Sphaerocarpos.*

Even though liverworts and mosses are widespread, they are apparently limited in size and distribution by their lack of vascular tissues. The earth has been colonized more successfully by plants that have these conducting tissues.

The Structure
of Vascular Plants

CHAPTER FIVE

In beginning our discussion of the land * plants in the preceding chapter, we stated that they include two major groups: The first of these, the liverworts and mosses, lack vascular tissue (xylem and phloem) and are, without exception, haploid, sexual plants with physically attached sporophytes. The second group is by far the larger; normally its members are diploid, spore-producing plants with well-developed vascular tissue. The sexual alternant (gametophyte) in their life cycle may be free-living and photoautrophic, or heterotrophic; in the latter case it is either saprophytic, or parasitic within the sporophyte. It has been suggested that in some of the first land plants the sporophytes became more complex during life on land, while the gametophytes (sexual phase), in contrast, became smaller, shorter-lived, and less active in somatic or vegetative functions. In other organisms, such as mosses and liverworts, the gametophyte remained dominant while the sporophytic phase became reduced and physically attached to

* Nature mocks at human categories. Most liverworts, mosses, and vascular plants are terrestrial, but a few are aquatic. Conversely, both aquatic and terrestrial algae and fungi are known.

it. Another theory holds that mosses and liverworts are descended from gametophytic algae which migrated to the land and that the vascular plants, in contrast, are derived from migrant algal sporophytes. The fossil record has not contributed materially to the resolution of these conflicting viewpoints.

Whatever their origin, the vascular plants display a degree of complexity that is unmatched by nonvascular plants. Accordingly, the present chapter will be devoted to a brief, general introduction to the gross and microscopic structures of the vascular plants in general. In the following four chapters we shall be primarily concerned with a more specific description of the vegetative organs and of the reproductive process in representative vascular plants.

A wide range of morphological form and complexity exists among vascular plants. Among the smallest of these is the duckweed, *Lemna* (a flowering plant) (Fig. 5-1), a minute, floating aquatic plant. At the other extreme are the woody vines, shrubs, and trees, climaxed by such long-lived giants as the redwood trees, *Sequoia* and *Sequoiadendron,* and certain species of *Eucalyptus.* Between these extremes occurs a vast assemblage of species intermediate in size. These may be annual, with maturity, reproduction, and death occurring in one growing season, or perennial, with the individual plant persisting for more than one season. In spite of the tremendous range, all individual vascular plants begin their existence as single-celled zygotes * and achieve their final size by successive divisions of the zygote and its descendants, just as you and I did.

Growth involves increase in volume; it is accomplished most frequently by increase in cell number and cell size and is usually accompanied by *differentiation* (the modification of individual cells or tissues in accordance with function). The explanation of the mechanism of growth and differ-

---

* Exceptions are organisms propagated vegetatively—i.e., from cuttings, buds, or grafts—or those that reproduce without union of gametes, as in *Cyrtomium* (the holly fern), the common dandelion, and certain grasses.

Fig. 5-1. Lemna perpusilla, a floating, aquatic seed plant. (Courtesy Drs. William Hillman and John H. Miller.)

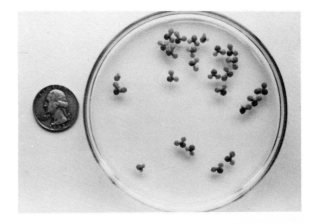

entiation among the cellular progeny of a single zygote to form a complex organism is one of the challenging problems of current biology awaiting solution. Growth in plants may be either generalized or localized. The axes of vascular plants, usually composed of *stems* and *roots,* develop from *promeristems* (Figs. 5-2 and 5-3), which are stem and root tips where cells are actively dividing. In some axes, in addition, *intercalary* regions of dividing cells persist, localized between base and apex, as at the joints in grass stems. Intercalary meristems often give rise to roots when stem cuttings are placed in moist sand or soil.

The next two sections offer a more detailed discussion of the processes of growth and differentiation in the vegetative organs of vascular plants, namely, stems, roots, and leaves.

ONTOGENY OF AXES (STEMS AND ROOTS)

In most plants, stems seem to be the most obvious, dominant portion of the axis; exceptions are bulbous plants (such as onions, lilies) and ferns other than tree ferns. In these, the leaves appear to be dominant. Leaves are produced at nodes spaced at intervals called internodes. In contrast, the root portion of the axis lacks leaves and, accordingly, definite nodes and internodes.

The promeristem of stems is usually concealed (Figs. 5-2 and 5-4) by the numerous minute, developing leaves it bears. In this immature region, the internodes are very short. Together, the promeristem and developing leaves form a bud. In woody plants, where growth is seasonal and periodic, certain leaves develop into impervious, protective *bud scales* (Fig. 5-4). In roots, on the other hand, the apex is covered by a mantle of cells, the *root-cap* (Fig. 5-3).

The cells of the promeristem divide rapidly, thus increasing cell number. Some distance back from the apex, cell multiplication ceases, and the cells enlarge and differentiate into functional *primary tissues*. In many herbaceous (soft-textured, green-stemmed) plants, these alone function throughout the existence of the individual.

As increase in cell size and change in form abate, specialized patterns of cell-wall deposition complete the process of differentiation into three types of primary tissue: (1) the vascular tissues composed of xylem and phloem (Figs. 5-5 and 5-6) and, sometimes the *cambium* (see p. 52); (2) the superficial epidermal layer; and (3) the remaining tissues, cortex and pith (if present) (Figs. 5-5 and 5-6). The primary vascular tissues of stems and roots are connected with the veins of leaves and of reproductive organs by branches of vascular tissue; these are called *traces.*

Xylem cells are often elongate and their walls are thickened with a mixture of lignin and cellulose; it is because of the lignification that they are hard. Xylem is a complex tissue consisting of several components. The conducting cells, *tracheids* and *vessels,* together with the fibers are dead at

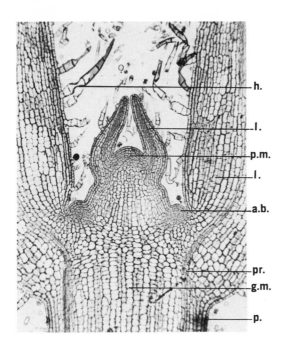

Fig. 5-2. Coleus blumei. **Median longitudinal section (m.l.s.) of the stem apex; (a.b., axillary bud; g.m., ground meristem; h., epidermal hair; l., leaf; p., protoderm (precursor of epidermis; p.m., promeristem, pr., procambium, precursors of vascular tissue and cambium).**

h.

l.

p.m.

l.

a.b.

pr.
g.m.

p.

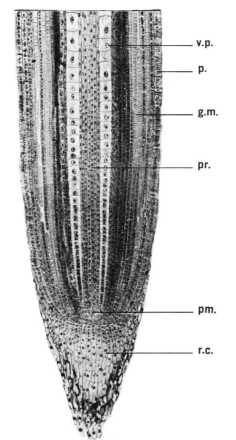

v.p.

p.

g.m.

pr.

pm.

r.c.

Fig. 5-3. Maize root top (Zea mays) **(g.m., ground meristem; p., protoderm; p.m., promeristem; pr., procambium; v.p., xylem vessel precursors; r.c., root cap). (Courtesy Drs. J. H. Leech and W. G. Whaley.)**

Fig. 5-4. Photinia: terminal bud.

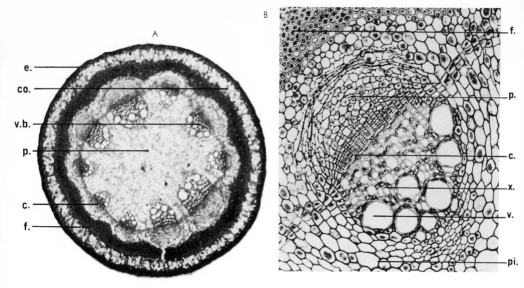

Fig. 5-5. Aristolochia **sp. (A) Transection of stem in region of primary permanent tissues, low magnification (c., cambium; co., cortex; e., epidermis; p., pith;
v.b., vascular bundle containing primary xylem within, separated by cambium
from the primary phloem without). (B) One vascular bundle and adjacent tissues; f., supporting fibers; p., phloem; pi., pith; v., vessel of xylem; x., xylem—
parenchyma and tracheids in region of label line).**

maturity (Figs. 5-7 and 5-8); some xylem cells, the parenchyma, remain
alive for a longer time. The major functions of xylem are support, and the
transport of water and the substances dissolved in it. Phloem, usually close
to the xylem, may contain lignified fibers, but its other components are
living cells with cellulose walls (Fig. 5-8). Most important of these are
the *sieve cells*—often united end-to-end in a pipe-like series, the *sieve
tube*—and the *companion cells,* if present. Phloem serves in the conduction
of complex substances manufactured in metabolism. In stems, the primary

**Fig. 5-6. Buttercup (Ranunculus), transection of root. (A) At low magnification
(c., cortex; e., epidermis; s., stele, or xylem and phloem); (B) Enlarged view of
s. and adjacent regions (en., endodermis; p., phloem; pe., pericycle; x., xylem).**

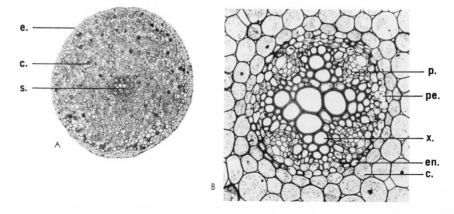

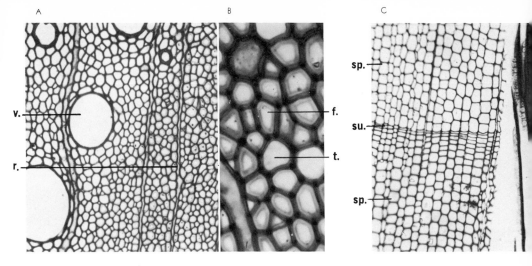

Fig. 5-7. Xylem, or wood. (A) Oak (Quercus velutina), **transection: r., ray; (B) Portion of oak transection enlarged; note fibers (f.) and tracheids (t.); (C) White pine** (Pinus strobus), **at left in transection, at right in longitudinal (radial) section showing pitted tracheids (sp., large-celled xylem formed early in growing season; su., small-celled xylem formed at end of growing season. Spring and summer xylem of one growing season constitute an annual ring).**

xylem and phloem are either *concentric* or *collateral* (opposite each other) (Fig. 5-5); in roots, they alternate in a radial pattern (Fig. 5-6).

In some axes the center is occupied by a pith composed of thin-walled cellulosic parenchyma cells, which may function in storage (Figs. 5-5 and 5-10). The tissues lying between the vascular tissues and the epidermis vary in extent and complexity. Just adjacent to the xylem and phloem of roots (and in some stems) lies the *pericycle* (Fig. 5-6). In roots, the pericycle has the important function of initiating branching. In most roots, in the stems of many seedless vascular plants, and in the fleshy, prostrate stems (rhizomes) of some seed plants, an *endodermis* (Fig. 5-6) may surround the vascular region and pericycle. The remaining tissues of the axis, except for the epidermis, constitute the *cortex* (Figs. 5-5 and 5-6). In general, the cortex is a storage region, although it is photosynthetic in young stems and aerial roots.

Epidermal cells (Fig. 5-9) are living cells whose outer walls may be modified in various ways. In most roots, they may protrude to form tubular, absorptive *root hairs* (Fig. 5-9A); in stems, they may develop into various types of glandular and nonglandular hairs and scales (Fig. 5-9B,C). The outer walls of epidermal cells of aerial (i.e., not in soil) organs usually are covered with an impervious *cuticle* composed of a waxy substance, *cutin*. Intercellular spaces between epidermal cells, together with the bordering *guard cells,* are known as *stomata* (Fig. 5-13). These are the main pathways of gaseous interchange, although this interchange also occurs through the cuticle and outer epidermal cell walls.

The preceding paragraphs have summarized the development and structure of the primary tissues, the origin of which may be traced to the apical meristem. In some herbaceous and in all woody plants, *secondary tissues* are added to the primary tissues after elongation of the axis at a given level has ceased (Fig. 5-10). The extent and duration of this process of *secondary growth* vary with the species. Thus, in such long-lived trees as *Sequoia* and *Sequoiadendron,* secondary growth has been occurring for several thousand years in some individuals. Were it not for this process, lumber as we know it would not exist.

Secondary growth depends on the active division of a layer of cells, the *cambium* (Figs. 5-5B, 5-10C), lying between the xylem and phloem. Most of the cells formed by the cambium differentiate into *secondary xylem* between the cambium and primary xylem (s.x., Fig. 5-10), fewer turn into *secondary phloem* cells between the cambium and primary phloem (s.p., Fig. 5-10). The activity of the cambium is seasonal, and in perennial woody plants this is reflected in the depositing of the secondary xylem as *annual rings,* or cylinders (a.r., Fig. 5-10). Increase of the internal portion of the stem by cambial activity ruptures the epidermis and cortex which are gradually replaced by corky layers, the *periderm.* As secondary growth continues, the cracks in the outer tissue cut more deeply and additional layers of periderm form. Accordingly, the bark of woody plants may become complex consisting of strips of periderm and other tissues such as cortex and phloem.

Secondary xylem is *wood.* The hardness of wood is caused basically by lignin and cellulose thickening the cell walls, the degree of hardness depending on the amount of lignification and the percentage of thick-walled

Fig. 5-8. Vascular tissue. (A) Transection of portion of vascular bundle from stem of maize (Zea mays) (c.c., companion cell; s.t., sieve tube of phloem—note sieve plate in one sieve tube; v., xylem vessel); (B) l.s., vascular tissue of squash (Cucurbita) (s.t., sieve tube of phloem; t., xylem tracheid with helical lignification; v., xylem vessel showing remains of dissolved transverse walls).

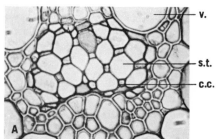

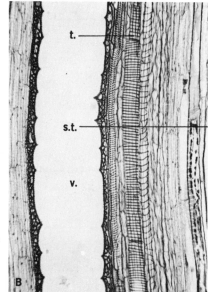

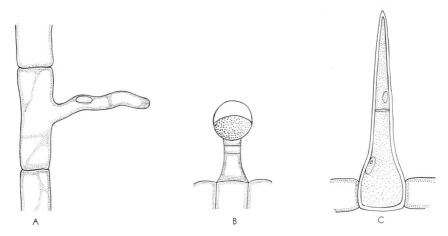

Fig. 5-9. Epidermal hairs. (A) Root hair of barley; (B) Glandular and (C) non-glandular hairs of geranium.

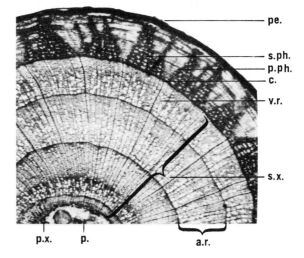

Fig. 5-10. Basswood (Tilia americana) sector of transection of 5-year-old stem (a.r., annual ring of secondary xylem; c., cambium; p., pith; pe., corky periderm which has replaced epidermis; p.ph., primary phloem; p.x., primary xylem covered by secondary xylem (s.x.) added by cambium; s.ph., secondary phloem; v.r., vascular ray).

pe.
s.ph.
p.ph.
c.
v.r.
s.x.
p.x.   p.   a.r.

fibers present. The grain and markings in wood depend on the way the annual rings and rays have been cut and exposed.

MORPHOLOGY OF LEAVES

Leaves arise as localized mounds of tissue near the promeristem and are called *leaf primordia* (Fig. 5-2). In contrast with axes, most leaves are simple, but there is some evidence that the simplicity may be deceptive and a result of secondary simplification from more complex beginnings, a phenomenon known as *reduction*. At one extreme, true leaves, those with vascular tissue (Figs. 6-7 and 6-8), approach moss leaves in size; at the other, are the enormous leaves of tree ferns, palms, and bananas. Large leaves with branching veins (vascular tissues) generally are interpreted to be equivalent to branches of the axis that, during the course of evolution, have become flattened, the tissues having extended between the branches

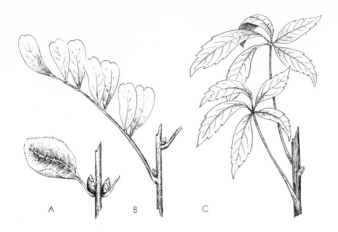

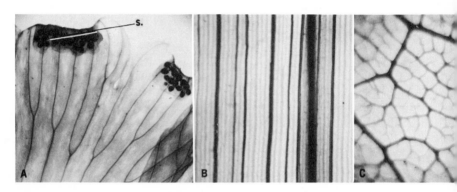

Fig. 5-11. Leaf structure. (A) Simple leaf, Euonymus sp.; (B) Pinnately compound leaf, Sophora sp.; (C) Palmately compound leaves, Scheffeleria.

Fig. 5-12. Venation patterns. (A) Dichotomous venation in maidenhair fern (Adiantum) (s., sporangia covered by folded leaf margin); (B) Parallel venation in Cyperus; (C) Netted venation in Sophora. (Courtesy Professors H. W. Bischoff and D. A. Larson.)

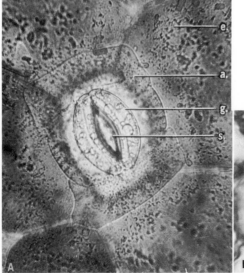

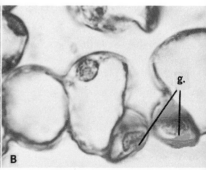

Fig. 5-13. Stomata. (A) Surface view of stoma of leaf of Rhoeo discolor (a., accessory cell; e., epidermal cell; g., guard cell; s., stoma); (B) Transection of stoma of Privet (Ligustrum) leaf (see Fig. 5-14).

by a sort of webbing. Certain small leaves with unbranched veins are thought to be fundamentally different from these; the simplicity of others may be a manifestation of evolutionary reduction from more complex types.

In external form, leaves may have whole or divided blades (Fig. 5-11); the former are *simple* and the latter *compound* leaves. The *petiole* (leaf stalk) of compound leaves thus bears a number of *leaflets* which are shed as a unit with the petiole. Furthermore, buds occur only at the base of the petiole in both simple and compound leaves, not at the bases of the leaflet stalks. Various types of compound leaves occur, the common ones being either *palmately* or *pinnately* (Fig. 5-11B,C) compound.

Leaf blades are traversed by an extensive system of veins, which are the ultimate branches of the vascular traces. Several patterns of *venation* are common, among them *dichotomous, parallel,* and *netted* types (Fig. 5-12).

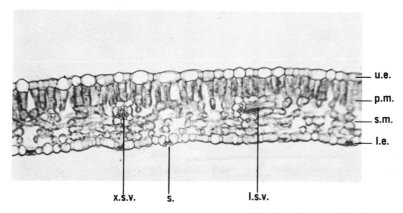

Fig. 5-14. Privet (Ligustrum) leaf, sector of a transection (l.e., lower epidermis; l.s.v., longisection of a vein; p.m., palisade mesophyll; s., stoma in section; s.m., spongy mesophyll; u.e., upper epidermis; x.s.v., transection of a vein).

Most leaves are relatively simple internally as compared with axes. Secondary growth is limited, if it occurs, and affects only the vascular tissues. The leaf surfaces are covered by an epidermis, more or less waxy and impervious and possessing stomata (Figs. 5-13 and 5-14). The intervening tissues (Fig. 5-14), known as *mesophyll,* frequently may be differentiated into an upper series of columnar cells, the *palisade mesophyll,* and a lower one of loosely contiguous cells, the *spongy mesophyll.* The mesophyll cells are rich in chloroplasts and active in photosynthesis. None of the mesophyll cells is far-removed from a vein, so that active transfer of substances to and away from the photosynthesizing mesophyll cells is possible. Leaves differ in texture, in degree of cutinization, and in the amount of supporting tissues present. Finally, they vary also in their pattern of attachment to the stem and in their arrangement in the bud.

With respect to leaves, plants may be *evergreen* (never completely without leaves) or *deciduous*. In the latter case, *all* the leaves are shed periodically. Leaf fall is accomplished usually by the formation of a special separating layer, the *abscission layer,* which severs the leaf at its base or at the base of the petiole. In certain regions, especially northeastern America and Scandinavia, the leaf fall of deciduous trees is preceded by the phenomenon of autumnal coloration. The chlorophyll of the leaves disintegrates, leaving the yellow-orange pigments (carotenes and xanthophylls), which increase in amount. Scarlet coloration often reflects development of the pigment *anthocyanin* in the cell vacuoles.

Seedless Vascular Plants I

CHAPTER SIX

Vascular plants include two major types, one seedless and one seed-bearing. The fossil remains of seedless vascular plants have been identified with certainty in rock strata as ancient as early Devonian (Fig. 6-1). Both seedless and seed-bearing types have persisted to the present day.

The presence of vascular tissue in the diploid sporophytic phase of the vascular plants has been widely interpreted as evidence of kinship through descent from a common precursor. Accordingly, these plants often are classified in a single division, the *Tracheophyta* (Table 1-1), a name that emphasizes the presence of vascular tissue. This emphasis upon and significance attached to vascular tissue have not been universally accepted, however (see Table 1-1); some students of plant relationships (*phylogeny*) consider the widespread occurrence of vascular tissue to be a manifestation of parallel evolution. Proponents of this interpretation classify the vascular plants in a number of separate groups whose ranks vary with the classifier (Table 1-1).

Whatever rank assigned to them, there is almost unanimous agreement that the seedless vascular plants include four major groups: (1) the leafless psilophytes; (2) the club and spike "mosses"; (3) the arthrophytes; and (4) the ferns. We shall discuss the first three of these groups in the present chapter and the fourth in the following one. In the next two chapters after that we shall consider the seed plants, both gymnosperms and angiosperms.

Fig. 6-1. Major stratigraphic and time divisions and occurrence of major plant groups.

Era	System or Period	Series or Epoch	Estimated ages of time boundaries in millions of years.	Probable time of origin and existence of plant groups
Cenozoic	Quaternary	Recent		
		Pleistocene	1.5	
	Tertiary	Pliocene	12	
		Miocene	25	
		Oligocene	34	
		Eocene	60	
		Paleocene		
Mesozoic	Cretaceous	Upper (Late) / Lower (Early)	132	
	Jurassic	Upper (Late) / Middle (Middle) / Lower (Early)	180	Angiosperms
	Triassic	Upper (Late) / Middle (Middle) / Lower (Early)	225	
Paleozoic	Permian		275	Gymnosperms
	Carboniferous systems — Pennsylvanian	Upper (Late) / Middle (Middle) / Lower (Early)	310	
	Carboniferous systems — Mississippian	Upper (Late) / Lower (Early)	350	Mosses
	Devonian	Upper (Late) / Middle (Middle) / Lower (Early)	405	Liverworts / Psilophytes / Lycopods / Arthrophytes / Pterophytes
	Silurian	Upper (Late) / Middle (Middle) / Lower (Early)	430	
	Ordovician	Upper (Late) / Middle (Middle) / Lower (Early)	485	
	Cambrian	Upper (Late) / Middle (Middle) / Lower (Early)	600	
Pre-Cambrian			1700 ... 4500	Algae and fungi

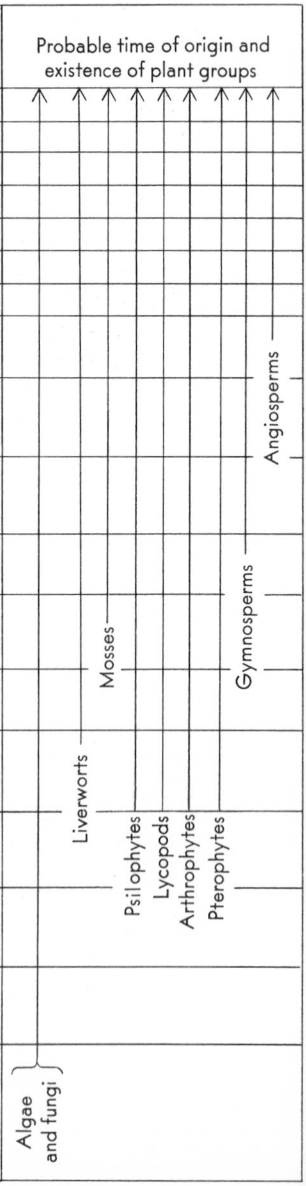

Fig. 6-2. Rhynia Gwynne-Vaughani, a middle Devonian (see Fig. 6-1) fossil vascular plant (s., sporangium). (Courtesy Chicago Natural History Museum.)

In the extinct Devonian (Fig. 6-1) flora, there were several vascular plants without leaves and roots. These are known to us through well-preserved specimens such as *Rhynia* (Fig. 6-2) and *Psilophyton*. The subterranean stems (rhizomes) of these plants bore unicellular absorptive protuberances, called rhizoids, from their epidermal cells. Sections of these fossilized axes reveal that the vascular tissues were entirely primary in origin. Certain lateral branches ended in sporangia where the presence of tetrads indicates that the spores arose by meiosis and that the organisms which produced them were sporophytes.

Among extant plants, *Psilotum* (the Whisk Fern) (Fig. 6-3), is one of a very few plants that display similar organization. *Psilotum* is tropical and

Fig. 6-3. Psilotum nudum. **(A) Potted plant; (B) Longitudinal section of stem and branch with sporangium; dark cells in latter are spore mother cells or sporocytes.**

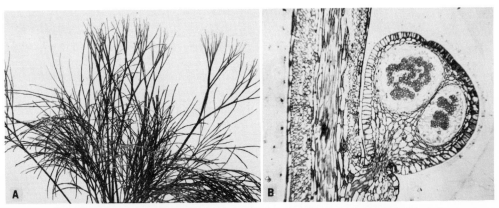

Fig. 6-4. Psilotum nudum: **portion of branch with sporangia, enlarged.**

Fig. 6-5. Psilotum. **Transection of stem (c., cortex; e., epidermis; en., endodermis; s., stoma; vt., vascular tissue.**

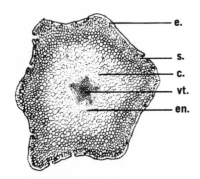

subtropical in habitat and sometimes epiphytic, that is, it grows upon other plants, using them only for support. *Psilotum nudum* is an herbaceous dichotomously branching plant approximately two feet in height. Its ridged axes, both the erect ones and the rhizomes, contain vascular tissue (Fig. 6-5). The stem is the photosynthetic organ, as it is in such plants as cacti; the outermost portion of the cortex is composed of cells rich in chloroplasts, and the heavily cutinized epidermis is interrupted by stomata and guard cells (Fig. 6-5). The rhizome bears unicellular rhizoids.

In mature plants, many of the axes become fertile and produce trilobed sporangia on very short lateral branches (Figs. 6-3 and 6-4). Meiosis in *Psilotum,* as in mosses, liverworts, and all vascular plants, occurs when the spores arise in the sporangia in groups of four from the diploid sporocytes, or spore mother cells. When the spores have matured, the sporangia crack open and the smooth-walled spores are disseminated. As in all plants with sporic meiosis and morphological alternation of generations (p. 15), the spores in further development produce the sexual, haploid, gametophytic phase. In *Psilotum,* this is a minute, subterranean cylindrical structure (Fig. 6-6A) devoid of chlorophyll; it is, therefore, saprophytic, and, in some instances, only its antheridia and archegonia (Fig. 6-6A,B) enable one to distinguish it with certainty from juvenile sporophytic axes. Following fertilization, which is effected by multiflagellate sperms, the zygote undergoes nuclear and cell division to form a young sporophyte,

which at first is attached to the gametophyte. Development of the gametophyte from the spore and of the sporophyte from the zygote are rather
slow processes in *Psilotum.*

Psilotum and the extinct fossil plants that are similar in organization,
the psilophytes (Fig. 6-2) are unique among vascular plants in lacking
both roots and leaves. Most botanists interpret them as primitive plants
that are not greatly modified from their hypothetical, sporophytic, algal
progenitors.

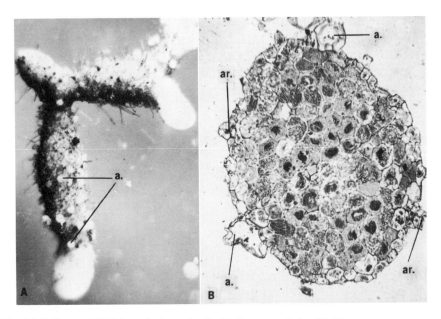

Fig. 6-6. Psilotum. (A) Enlarged view of cylindrical gametophyte; (B) Transection of gametophyte (a., antheridia; ar., archegonia). (Courtesy Professor David
Bierhorst.)

CLUB AND SPIKE "MOSSES"

A second line of seedless vascular plants with Devonian (Fig. 6-1) precursors are the club and spike "mosses." They have been called "mosses"
because living species are for the most part small-leaved, herbaceous plants.
The "club" and "spike" portions of their names refer to the localization
of spore-bearing structures, called *sporophylls,* at the tips of certain
branches with short internodes; these branches are known as *strobili* (Figs.
6-7A, 6-8B,C).

Two common genera, *Lycopodium* (Fig. 6-7A) and *Selaginella* (Fig.
6-8), which belong to this group, are rather widely distributed in both
temperate and tropical habitats. Species of *Lycopodium,* familiarly known

as "ground pine" and "trailing evergreen," are abundant on the floor of coniferous forests. Many species of *Selaginella* are more hydric in habitat than *Lycopodium,* but a few, like the familiar "resurrection plant," survive in arid soils. The plants may be either prostrate, forming ground covers, or erect, or pendulous epiphytes. A third genus, the aquatic or amphibious *Isoetes* (Fig. 6-7B), the "quillwort," is sometimes classified with the club mosses.

A comparison of the plant body of the club mosses with that of the psilophytes at once reveals two striking differences—namely, in the club mosses, unlike the psilophytes, vascularized leaves and roots are present. The axes elongate by growth of the apexes and produce a profusion of small, moss-like leaves, each with a single, unbranched vein. Leaves with single, unbranched veins, whose traces do not leave marked gaps as they leave the vascular system of the stem, are called *microphyllous.*

Fig. 6-7. (A) Lycopodium ob-
scurum (s., strobilus); (B)
Isoetes lithophila.

The sporangia of club mosses are borne at or near the bases of leaves and on their upper (adaxial) surfaces (Fig. 6-9). Such fertile leaves are known as sporophylls. In some species of *Lycopodium,* there is evidence that every leaf potentially is a sporophyll, but in many others, and in *Selaginella,* only the apical leaves of certain branches are fertile and associated in strobili (Figs. 6-7 and 6-8B,C). A strobilus, then, is a stem with short internodes and spore-bearing appendages. Each sporangium produces a number of fertile, *sporogenous* cells; these enlarge, often separate from one another, become spherical, and function as sporocytes. The latter un-

Fig. 6-8. Selaginella. (A) S. kraussiana, a creeping species; (B) S. sprengeri, portion of a plant with strobili, s.; (C) Strobilus of B, enlarged.

dergo meiosis and give rise to tetrads of haploid spores. When the spores have matured, the sporangia develop fissures through which the spores are disseminated.

The spores, under suitable conditions, develop into the haploid, sexual, gametophytic stage of the organism, in which gamete union and zygote production occur to initiate a new sporophytic generation. The homothallic gametophytes of *Lycopodium* (Fig. 6-10) are rather fleshy structures, in some species subterranean, devoid of chlorophyll, and saprophytic. In others, the gametophytes have some chlorophyll.

Sporogenesis in *Selaginella* is especially significant and instructive. In *Selaginella*, a number of the sporophylls of a given strobilus produce sporangia whose development is essentially like that described above (and like

Fig. 6-9. (A) Sporophyll of Lycopodium; (B) Microsporophyll; (C) Megasporophyll of Selaginella.

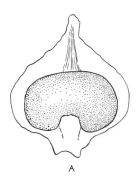
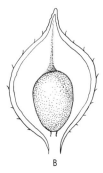
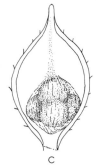

that described earlier in *Psilotum*), so that a large number of spores is produced (Fig. 6-9B). In other sporangia in the strobili of *Selaginella,* however, development of most of the sporocytes is arrested before meiosis; in most cases, only one sporocyte in such sporangia completes the meiotic process; the remainder degenerate. As the one spore tetrad forms, there is available a vast amount of nutritive material originally incorporated within the aborted spore mother cells. This material, apparently, is absorbed by the members of the single tetrad, with the result that they enlarge enormously until they actually distend the sporangial wall (Figs. 6-9C and 6-11). These large spores are called *megaspores.* The cells from which they arise are *megasporocytes.* In contrast, the ordinary-sized spores have come to be called *microspores,* although they are about the same size as the spores of many other plants that lack spore dimorphism, or *heterospory.* The sporangia that bear megaspores are *megasporangia* on *megasporophylls,* while the microspores arise in *microsporangia* on *microsporophylls. Selaginella,* with its two kinds of spores, is *heterosporous,* whereas *Lycopodium, Psilotum,* mosses, and liverworts are *homosporous. Isoetes* also is heterosporous.

In all heterosporous plants, microspores develop into *male gametophytes* and megaspores into *female gametophytes.* Development of the male and female gametophytes in *Selaginella* takes place largely within the spores (Fig. 6-12) and sporangia, and only in the later stages are the gametophyte-containing spores shed. The male and female gametophytes of *Selaginella* are reduced * in size and in extent of vegetative tissues. The male gametophytes consist largely of an antheridium that contains biflagellate sperms (Fig. 6-12A–C); the female gametophyte has some sterile cells and rhizoids and a cluster of archegonia (Fig. 6-12D–F). Both gametophytes are achlorophyllous and saprophytic, their nutrition being based on substances stored within the microspores and megaspores by the parent sporophyte. As a result of fertilization, usually one zygote of a given female gametophyte gives rise to a juvenile sporophyte (Fig. 6-13), thus completing the life cycle.

A number of phenomena that occur in *Selaginella* characterize both extinct fossil seedless vascular plants and extant seed-bearing plants. These include localization of

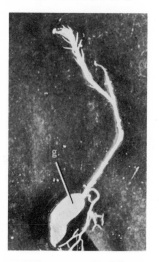

Fig. 6-10. Lycopodium sp.: **young sporophyte attached to carrot-shaped gametophyte, g.**

* As compared with the sexual phases of *Psilotum* (Fig. 6-6), *Equisetum* (Fig. 6-18A), and the ferns (Fig. 7-6B).

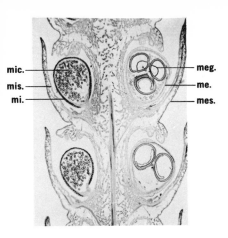

Fig. 6-11. Selaginella: **portion of a l.s. of the strobilus (me., megasporangium; meg., megaspore; mes., megasporophyll; mi., microsporangium; mic., microspore; mis., microsporophyll).**

sporangium-bearing appendages in *strobili, heterospory,* intrasporal and intrasporangial development of the gametophytes, and heterothallism.

Although extant club mosses like *Lycopodium* and *Selaginella* are small herbaceous plants, some of their extinct fossil cousins achieved tree-like proportions. This is true of such genera as *Lepidodendron* and *Sigillaria* (Fig. 6-14), which rested on branching bases and approached forest trees in height. These plants were perennial and had active cambia.

ARTHROPHYTES

A third group of seedless vascular plants, far more widespread and abundant in Pennsylvanian times (Fig. 6-1) than at present, is represented in our living flora only by *Equisetum* (Fig. 6-15). Species of this genus are known as "horsetails,"

Fig. 6-12. Selaginella: **development of the male (A–C) and female (D–E) gametophytes and embryo (F) (arch., archegonium; e-1, e-2, embryonic sporophytes; f.g., female gametophyte; m.g., male gametophyte; me.w., megaspore wall; mi.w., microspore wall; rh., rhizoids).**

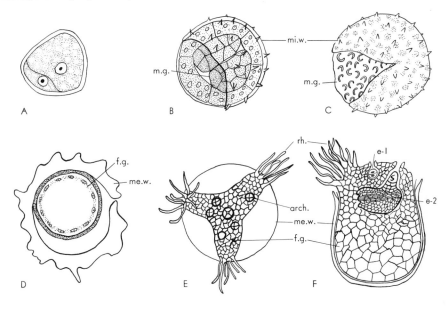

Fig. 6-13. Selaginella: **young sporophyte, s., attached to ♀ gametophyte within megaspore, m. (r., root).**

"pipes," and "scouring rushes," the last name being inspired by the siliceous texture of the species. Both woody and herbaceous arthrophytes inhabited the earth in Pennsylvanian times. Their fossil remains are at once recognizable by the whorled arrangement of the branches and fertile appendages (Figs. 6-14C, S; 6-15, 6-16, and 6-17). The clearly defined nodes and internodes give the plants a jointed appearance and have suggested the name "arthrophytes." As in the tree-like fossil relatives of the club mosses, cambial activity added secondary xylem over the primary vascular skeleton; in other words, the axes were quite woody.

The whorled habit of growth is well illus-

Fig. 6-14. **Reconstruction of a coal age (Pennsylvanian) forest (C.,** Calamites **sp., a giant arthrophytan plant; L.,** Lepidodendron, **a tree-like form reminiscent of** Lycopodium **and** Selaginella; **S.** Sphenophyllum **sp., an herbaceous genus; Sf., an unidentified seed fern; Si.,** Sigillaria, **a tree-like form reminiscent of** Lycopodium **and** Selaginella **and related to** Lepidodendron. **(Courtesy Illinois State Museum.)**

Fig. 6-15. Equisetum. (A) **Vegetative plants;** (B) **Fertile branches of** E. arvense **with strobili;** (C) E. hyemale, **vegetative axils with terminal strobili.**

Fig. 6-16. Equisetum. (A) E. hyemale, **detail of node and two adjacent internodes (l., leaf; b., bud);** (B) E. arvense, **sporangiophore and sporangia.**

Fig. 6-17. Equisetum arvense. (A) **Enlarged view of strobilus, the one at left being ready to shed spores and showing sporangia;** (B) **spores and spore germination of** E. hyemale; **(e., elaters; r., rhizoid).**

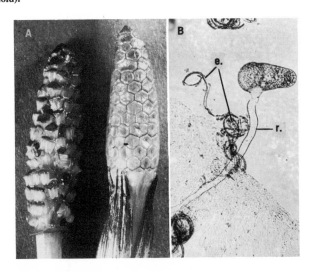

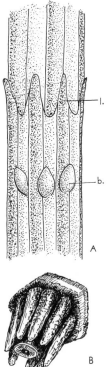

trated by branching species of *Equisetum* (Fig. 6-15A); in these, a circle of branches arises at a given node. The nodes of *Equisetum* are marked by a leaf sheath composed of a number of minute, tooth-like leaves joined at their bases (Fig. 6-16A). The photosynthetic activity of the leaves is negligible, the bulk of photosynthesis occurring in the vertical, ribbed stems, as in *Psilotum*. The aerial stems arise from deeply subterranean rhizomes that bear whorls of wiry roots. The roots and stems of *Equisetum* develop from apical meristems in which prominent apical cells function.

As in many club mosses, the sporangia of *Equisetum* are localized in strobili (Figs. 6-15C and 6-17). In the common *E. arvense,* the strobiliferous branches (Fig. 6-17A), which appear early in the spring, usually lack chlorophyll. As they shed their spores, the green vegetative shoots develop from other buds on the same rhizome. In such evergreen species as *E. hyemale,* by contrast, the strobili arise at the tips of the vegetative shoots as the latter mature (Fig. 6-15C). The appendages that bear the sporangia in *Equisetum* are known as *sporangiophores,* rather than sporophylls, inasmuch as good evidence from the study of fossils indicates they are not leaf-like. Each sporangiophore bears from 5 to 10 cylindrical sporangia on its adaxial surface (Fig. 6-16B). As usual, these contain sporogenous tissues within their walls, which give rise successively during maturation to sporocytes, tetrads, and mature spores as the meiotic process takes place. The homosporous spores of *Equisetum* are remarkable because of their appendages, the *elaters,* which arise by cracking of the outermost layer of the spore wall (Fig. 6-17B). These appendages are exceedingly sensitive to moisture, contracting and expanding with slight varia-

Fig. 6-18. (A) Equisetum hyemale, **gametophyte, living; (B)** E. hyemale, **gameto-phyte with young sporophytes attached.**

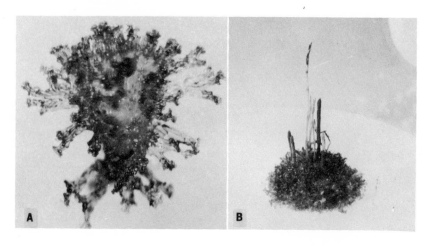

tions in relative humidity. The spores are liberated from the strobili by elongation of their internodes, curvature of the sporangiophore stalks, and bursting of the sporangia.

The richly chlorophyllous spores of *Equisetum* develop rapidly on moist soil into minute mound-like, green gametophytes (Fig. 6-18A). These grow at their margins and produce dorsal, membranous outgrowths on which and between the bases of which the antheridia (Fig. 6-18A) and archegonia (Fig. 6-18B) are borne. Rhizoids penetrate the substratum. Following fertilization by one of the multiflagellate sperms, one or more zygotes of a given gametophyte initiate development of the sporophytic (Fig. 6-18B), stage, thus completing the life cycle.

The psilophytes, club mosses, and *Equisetum* stem from ancient lines of plant life with but a few remnants in our present flora. The ferns, the fourth line of seedless vascular plants, although probably equally ancient in origin (Fig. 6-1), have been more successful in competing in the struggle for existence. We shall treat of the ferns in the next chapter, which will conclude with a comparative summary of all the seedless vascular plants.

Seedless Vascular Plants II: The Ferns

CHAPTER SEVEN

The representatives of the three groups of seedless vascular plants discussed in the preceding chapter were leafless (psilophytes) or microphyllous (club mosses, spike mosses, and arthrophytes). In striking contrast to these is the final group of seedless vascular plants, the ferns (Figs. 7-1 and 7-2), which along with the seed plants are *macrophyllous*. These leaves have branching veins and their traces leave gaps in the vascular tissues of the stem. Even in the mind of the layman, the fern leaf is the dominant organ of the plant; and this impression has a sound scientific foundation.

The ferns exhibit considerable diversity of growth habit and habitat. At one extreme are the large-leaved tree ferns with erect stems that grow in tropical rain forests; at the other are such small aquatic organisms as *Salvinia* (Fig. 7-9). A large group of ferns, intermediate in size, includes the familiar cultivated varieties and the natives of shady ravines and woodlands in both the temperate zone and the tropics. As a group, ferns are moisture- and shade-loving plants, although a few inhabit fissures in rocks in bright sunlight; these are subject to periodic desiccation, however. Ferns are, with the

Fig. 7-1. Dryopteris **sp.,** a **"shield fern":**
note rhizome buried by leaf bases, cir-
cinate young leaves, mature leaf and
roots.

Fig. 7-2. Adiantum capillus-veneris,
"Venus maidenhair fern."

rarest of exceptions, perennials. The ferns in the temperate zone survive from year to year by means of fleshy, often subterranean stems called rhizomes. The portions of the leaves above the soil die off to the level of the soil surface after frosts, and a new set of leaves, which was already present near the rhizome apex, is elevated the following spring.

The fern leaf is the dominant organ of the plant except perhaps in the tree ferns, in which it is challenged by the trunk-like stem. In a majority of ferns, the leaves have a unique arrangement in the bud known as *circinate verna-tion;* in this, the lower surface of the leaf during early development consistently develops more rapidly than the upper, resulting in the coiling of the leaf (Figs. 7-1 and 7-2). The large, circinately vernate leaves of certain ferns have suggested the name "fiddle head." Fern leaves may be either simple, with undivided blades, or variously compound, with divided blades attached to a *rachis*, the latter a prolongation of the petiole (Fig. 7-1). The upper and lower epidermal layers are cutinized, with stomata occurring predominantly in the lower layer, and they enclose a tissue rich in chloroplasts, the mesophyll. The latter is crossed by strands of xylem and phloem which form the veins.

The stems of most ferns other than tree ferns are prostrate and fleshy, at the surface of or under the soil. The wiry roots originate among the leaf bases (Figs. 7-1 and 7-2). The addition of secondary tissues by cambial activity is absent in most ferns. Even the stems of tree ferns are entirely primary in origin.

With few exceptions the conducting cells of the xylem of fern stems are single-celled tracheids; vessels (multicellular, perforated tubes) do occur, though, in the xylem of bracken fern, *Pteridium,* and in *Marsilea,* as they do sparingly in *Selaginella* and *Equisetum.*

Fig. 7-3. Ophioglossum vulga-tum, "adder's tongue fern."

As in all vascular plants, the plant itself is the sporophytic generation, and, accordingly, at maturity develops sporogenous tissue. In the ferns, this may be borne on a special spike (Fig. 7-3), on modified segments of leaves, or on the abaxial (under) surfaces of the vegetative leaves themselves (Fig. 7-4). The fertile regions on fern leaves that bear sporangia are known as *receptacles,* and the group of sporangia is called a *sorus.* In many species, but by no means in all, the sorus of sporangia is covered during development by a flap of tissue (Fig. 7-4A,B) or the inrolled margin of the leaf (Fig. 7-4C,D). These coverings are known as *true* and *false indusia,* respectively. The sporangia of some ferns are rather massive and thick-walled and produce numerous spores, as do those of the club and spike mosses and *Equisetum.* A few genera are heterosporous. In the more familiar ferns, like *Adiantum* and *Dryopteris,* the numerous sporangia, grouped in sori on the back of margins of the leaves, are comparatively small, thin-walled, and long-stalked (Fig. 7-5A); they produce only from 48 to 64 spores. The latter arise by meiosis from sporocytes, and at maturity their walls thicken with a dark brown, impervious substance turning the sori brown.

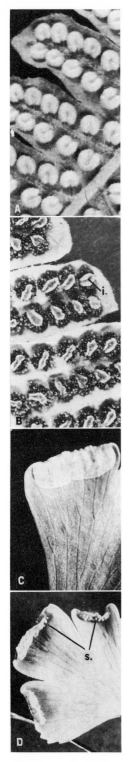

In species with indusia, these ultimately shrivel, exposing the sporangia when the spores have matured. The latter are ejected from the sporangia, which crack open (Fig. 7-5B) in a region of delicate *lip cells,* as the thickened cells of the *annulus,* a ring-like layer of cells, contract and then expand suddenly. Tremendous numbers of spores are produced by ferns, but the special requirements of moisture and shade of most species effectively reduce the number of developing gametophytes.

Spores that are deposited by air currents upon suitably moist soil and rocks germinate within 5 to 6 days (Fig. 7-6A) and commence development into the sexual phase, the gametophyte. The latter begins development as a small, algalike chain of cells, each filled with chloroplasts; often, there is a colorless rhizoid emerging from the basal cell of the chain. As growth continues, cell division in a second direction results in a membranous structure with an apical depression (Fig. 7-6B).

The central portion of the developing gametophyte is several cell layers thick, but the wings are one-layered. Additional rhizoids emerge from the cells of the ventral surface and penetrate the substratum. When the germinating spores are well separated, the resulting gametophytes are heart-shaped and may in some species approach one-half inch in diameter. The fern gametophyte was designated the *prothallus* or *prothallium* long ago, since it was known to be the precursor of the fern plant even before its sexual function was clearly understood.

Fig. 7-4. Spore production in ferns. (A,B) Immature, A, and mature, B, sori in Drypoteris, a shield fern (i., indusium shrivelled, exposing sporangia); (C,D) Immature and mature stages in maidenhair, Adiantum; the leaf margin covers the sporangia in C, while the sporangia, s., are exposed in D—all lower leaf surface. (See also Fig. 5-12A.)

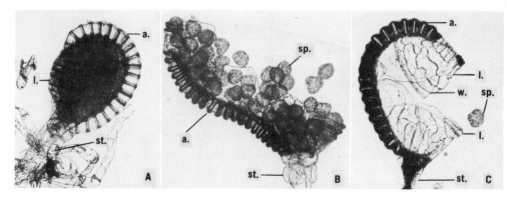

Fig. 7-5. Dryopteris sp. (A) Mature, intact sporangium; (B) Sporangium after contraction of annulus; (C) empty sporangium (a., annulus; l., lip cells; sp., spore; st., stalk; w., wall cells).

As well-nourished gametophytes mature—about 60 days after the spores have been planted in laboratory cultures—they develop both antheridia and archegonia on their ventral surfaces (Fig. 7-6C) and accordingly, are homothallic. Slight accumulations of moisture between the lower surface of the gametophyte and the substratum suffice to open both the antheridia, which discharge the multiflagellate sperm, and the necks of mature archegonia. The cells inside the necks of the maturing archegonia dissolve, thus providing a moist passageway through which the sperms swim to the ripe eggs. The eggs of several archegonia may be fertilized, but usually only one of the zygotes undergoes development into a juvenile sporophyte (Fig. 7-7).

This process, which is very rapid in the common garden and woodland ferns, is initiated by three successive nuclear and cell divisions of the zygote within the archegonium, forming what is called an octant. Two cells of the octant organize an embryonic root, the *radicle,* which rapidly grows out of the gametophyte and enters the soil. The two cells just above these

Fig. 7-6. Dryopteris. (A) Spore germination; (B) Gametophyte (prothallus 41 days old; (C) Ventral view of portion of mature gametophyte showing sex organs (a., antheridium; ar., archegonium; s., spore wall).

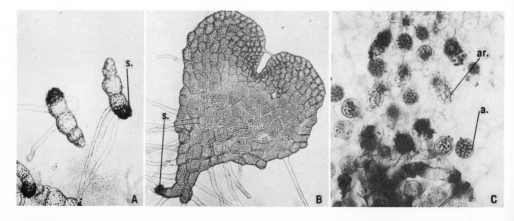

form by division a bulbous mass of tissues, the *foot,* which seems to function in absorption from the gametophyte. Of the other four cells, two rapidly organize the primary (or embryonic) leaf, or *cotyledon* (Fig. 7-7B). The other two cells grow and divide slowly, but they gradually organize the apex of a stem, which subsequently produces additional leaves. The first leaves differ from those of the mature sporophyte. As growth continues, later produced leaves finally resemble those typical of the species. When the minute sporophyte has become established, the membranous gametophyte disintegrates. The gametophyte generation, then, in the ferns, as in other seedless vascular plants, is relatively short-lived, simple in structure, and ephemeral. The sporophytic phase is dominant in the life cycle.

In a number of species of ferns, the gametophyte stage either fails to develop sex organs, or archegonia or antheridia may be lacking. In such cases, the vegetative tissue of the gametophyte below the apical notch, without fertilization, develops into a juvenile sporophyte that matures. This is the phenomenon of *apogamy,* the development of an embryo without union of gametes. In such ferns, sporophyte and gametophyte have the same chromosomal constitution, which is further evidence, as we noted in the mosses, that sporophytes and gametophytes are not merely results of different chromosomal number.

Several ferns are heterosporous, among them *Marsilea* and *Salvinia. Marsilea* (Fig. 7-8) is often mistaken for wood sorrel (sour grass) or four-leaved clover by the uninitiated. *Salvinia* (Fig. 7-9) is a minute, floating aquatic plant. In these heterosporous genera, the megaspores produce female, and the microspores male, gametophytes.

The economic importance of ferns resides for the most part in the aesthetic appeal of their foliage. They are widely used as ornamental plants both in temperate and tropical gardens and in conservatories. The large-leaved, finely divided (many times compound) species are highly prized by connoiseurs of foliage plants.

SUMMARY OF SEEDLESS VASCULAR PLANTS

With this brief account of the structure and reproduction of ferns, we have considered the last of the four groups of seedless vascular plants. These comprise the psilophytes (Figs. 6-2 through 6-6) (*Psilotum* and the

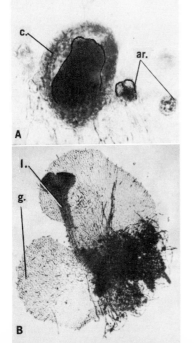

Fig. 7-7. Dryopteris: **development of the embryonic sporophyte. (A) Before emergence of sporophyte from the old archegonium or calyptra; (B) After emergence (ar., archegonium; c., calyptra; g., gametophyte; l., leaf).**

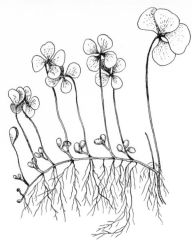

Fig. 7-8. Marsilea, **a heterosporous fern (Eames,** Morphology of Vascular Plants, **McGraw-Hill, 1936).**

Fig. 7-9. (A) Salvinia natans **and (B)** Azolla sp. **(both same magnification; note mm. scale); minute aquatic, heterosporous ferns.**

fossil *Rhynia* and *Psilophyton*); the club mosses (Figs. 6-7 through 6-13) (*Lycopodium, Selaginella, Isoetes,* and such fossil types as *Lepidodendron* and *Sigillaria*); the arthrophytes (Figs. 6-15 through 6-18) (*Equisetum* and the fossil *Calamites, Sphenophyllum,* and *Calamophyton*); and, finally, the ferns (Figs. 7-1 through 7-9).

These plants have in common the dominance of their sporophytic phase over the gametophytic one and their vascular tissue (attributes possessed also by seed plants). In the past, the four groups were classified as a single division of the plant kingdom (Table 1-1) designated as Pteridophyta, which is freely translated as "the ferns and their allies." The fossil record does not provide compelling evidence of alliance or common origin; instead, it indicates that these four series extend back into Devonian times (Fig. 6-1) and earlier.

The ferns differ from other seedless vascular plants in having large, complex leaves that are interpreted as modified branching axes. Such axes are thought to have limited branching to one plane and to have undergone an expansion of the softer tissues of the axes over the flattened vascular skeleton to form the leaf mesophyll. Macrophyllous leaves, then, like those of ferns and seed plants, however, simple, are interpreted as flattened and webbed branch systems. The microphyllous leaves of other seedless vascular plants, on the contrary, have been looked upon as mere localized emergencies of the axes, not far removed from thorns or the spines of psilophytes except by their vascular tissue; less frequently, microphyllous leaves have been interpreted as branch systems reduced in extent. When we consider, in retrospect, the leaves of seaweed (algae), mosses, liverworts, club mosses, arthrophytes, ferns, and seed plants, we might well pause to reflect whether all leaves are strictly homologous—that is, fundamentally similar in structure—just because they are called "leaves."

Gymnospermous Seed Plants

CHAPTER EIGHT

You will recall that plants may be divided into two great categories on the basis of whether or not they produce seeds. None of the plants discussed in the preceding chapters produce seeds. Algae, fungi, liverworts, and mosses are nonvascular seedless plants, whereas the psilophytes, club mosses, arthrophytes, and ferns do develop xylem and phloem. So do the members of the second great group, the seed-bearing plants.

Among the seed plants themselves, two types are clearly distinguishable; the distinctions primarily relate to the location of the seeds, but also to other attributes. In one type the seeds are usually borne *within* structures known as *fruits* (Fig. 8-1A,B,C). The latter may open at maturity and expose and shed seeds, but, at least in the early stages of development, the seeds are enclosed. Plants that bear their seeds in this manner are known as *angiosperms,* or "flowering plants" (Table 1-1). In the second group, the *gymnosperms,** the seeds develop on the surface of an appendage

* Although "Gymnospermae" has been abandoned by many as a formal taxon (Table 1-1), anglicized it is a useful descriptive term.

(which has various names) and are not enclosed by it (Fig. 8-1D,E). Although the seed-bearing structures of gymnosperms may occur in cones, or strobili (Figs. 8-1D,E and 8-2), so that the seeds are hidden from view, the seeds are not enclosed within the structures that bear them but merely concealed by the grouping and overlapping of those structures.

Gymnospermous plants are all woody, whether trees, shrubs, or vines; familiar examples include the pine, hemlock, spruce, fir, juniper, and cypress, the less familiar fern- and palm-like *cycads* (Fig. 8-8), and the maidenhair tree, *Ginkgo biloba* (Fig. 8-9). Among the flowering plants, in contrast, both woody and herbaceous types are abundant, but the herbaceous outnumber the woody in genera, species, and individuals. Stems of herbaceous plants are green and soft in texture because very little or no secondary xylem is added by the vascular cambium if, indeed, the latter is present at all (see Chapter 5). The difference, of course, is that in woody plants the vascular cambium adds annual increments of secondary xylem. Oaks, elms, maples, lilacs, roses, and grapes are woody angiosperms that are familiar to most people. Iris, grasses, daisies, tomatoes, and morning-glories all are herbaceous flowering plants.

The classification of seed-bearing plants, like that of other organisms, varies with the classifier (Table 1-1). The discovery of fossil fern-like leaves with attached seeds, representative of a group of extinct plants known as "seed ferns," suggested that seed-bearing plants derived from a common ancestry with ferns. This discovery, and the fact that seed ferns and other seed plants are macrophyllous, inspired their classification in a single taxon, the Pteropsida, which includes both ferns and seed plants. Other classifiers, including the author, look upon the ferns, seed plants, and even the gymnosperms and angiosperms as separate lines of evolutionary development and, accordingly, distribute them among several separate divisions of the plant kingdom.

The remainder of the present chapter will be taken up with an account of reproduction in gymnosperms and a consideration of certain representative types. In Chapter 9 we shall discuss the angiosperms in some detail.

REPRODUCTION IN GYMNOSPERMOUS SEED PLANTS

Before proceeding to an examination of reproduction in these plants, let us consider in general terms the reproductive process that results in the production of seeds. All seed plants, like all seedless vascular plants, are the sporophytic phase of the life cycle. Accordingly, at maturity, certain portions of the vegetative organism become fertile and produce spores. In many gymnosperms, as in the club mosses and *Equisetum,* the spore-bearing appendages are aggregated in localized regions of the axes to form cones, or strobili (Figs. 8-1D and 8-2). Recall that spores produced by the sporophytes of all land plants develop into the sexual, gametophytic phase of the plants' life cycles.

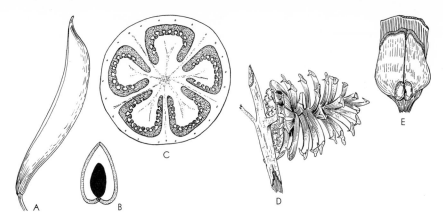

Fig. 8-1. Angiospermy (A–C) and gymnospermy (D–E). (A) Pod (fruit) of garden pea; (B) The same in transection showing enclosed seed; (C) Transection of tomato fruit with enclosed seeds; (D) Seed cone, or strobilus, of pine; (E) Portion of one of segments of D showing unenclosed, winged seeds.

Fig. 8-2. Pine: composite sketch of branch in spring-time (Me. 1, Megastrobilus at pollination; Me. 2, megastrobilus pollinated a year earlier; Me. 3, megastrobilus pollinated two years earlier, mature and shedding seeds; Mi., microstrolili; S., stem unfolding from terminal bud; S.a., stem apex).

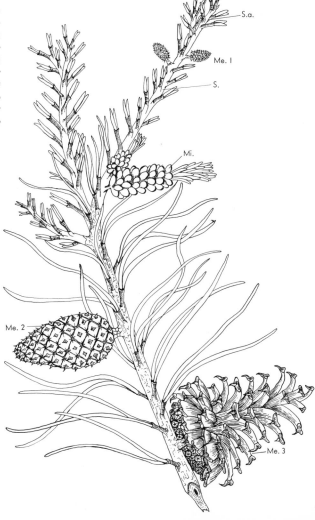

In connection with the present discussion, several phenomena that occur in *Selaginella* (pp. 62–65) are especially noteworthy. The spores of *Selaginella* are of two sizes and differ in their origin and in their subsequent development. The spores of ordinary size, the microspores, which are produced in large numbers in their sporangia, develop into male gametophytes. Other spores, the megaspores, of which only four are typically produced in a given sporangium, become filled with stored foods, enlarge tremendously, and, upon germination, produce female gametophytes. The production of two types of spores is known as heterospory. A further significant point in *Selaginella* is that the early stages of both the male and female gametophytes develop within the microspores and megaspores, respectively, so that the gametophytes are dependent for nutrition on materials stored in the spores. Under certain conditions, the spores may be retained within their sporangia until they have completed development into mature gametophytes and, rarely, even until after fertilization has occurred! In summary, then, we observe in *Selaginella* the presence of: (1) heterospory (involving tremendous size differences between the microspores and megaspores) and its inevitable corollary, (2) heterothallic gametophytes; (3) dependence of the developing gametophytes on nutrients from the sporophyte; (4) intrasporal development of the gametophytes; and (5) prolonged retention of the latter within the sporangia. With some modifications, these same phenomena, together with certain innovations, occur in reproduction leading to the formation of seeds.

All seed plants, as we have seen, produce two kinds of spores in different sporangia; those that grow into male gametophytes are usually called microspores, those that grow into female gametophytes, megaspores (although they do not differ markedly in size *). These spores of seed plants

* The megaspores of seed plants are not very different in terms of size from the microspores. Can we say, then, that the seed plants are heterosporous in the sense that seedless vascular plants are? The terms microspore and megaspore have been applied to the male-gametophyte-producing and female-gametophyte-producing spores of seed plants, respectively, in spite of their similarity in size. A suggested explanation of the similarity is that permanent retention of the megaspores within the megasporangium has reduced the size of the megaspore. According to another hypothesis, the spores are *homosporous,* but the gametophytes they produce are *heterothallic.*

Fig. 8-3. Pine. (A) Microsporophyll with two microsporangia; (B) Magnified aspect of single microspore with air bladders; (C) Appendage of megastrobilus with two ovules.

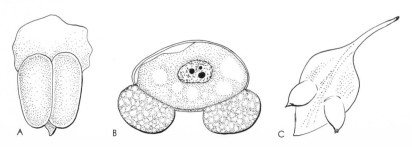

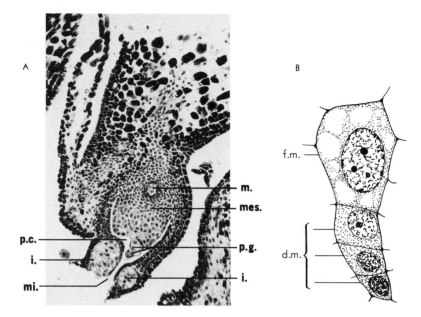

Fig. 8-4. Pinus virginiana. **(A) Ovule and its appendages in longitudinal section soon after pollination (i., integument; m., megasporocyte; mes., megasporangium; mi., micropyle; p.c., pollen chamber; p.g., pollen grain); (B) Functional megaspore, f.m., with degenerating products of meiosis, d.m.**

and the sporangia that produce them differ from those of *Selaginella* in several important aspects, which may be summarized as follows:

(1) The megasporangia in seed plants are surrounded by several layers of cells called the *integument* (sometimes a double layer); these covered megasporangia are called *ovules* (Fig. 8-3C).

(2) Of the four potential spores formed at meiosis, only one, the *functional megaspore,* survives (Fig. 8-4B).

(3) The surviving megaspore at maturity approximates the size of the microspore and lacks a markedly thickened wall and stored foods.

(4) The microspores are shed ultimately as *pollen grains,* which contain the male gametophyte; these grains are transferred, by various means, from the microsporangium to more or less close proximity to the ovule containing the megaspore and later the female gametophyte. This transfer is called pollination.

(5) The functional megaspore is *never* shed from its megasporangium.

(6) It completes its development there into a mature female gametophyte (Fig. 8-6A), using metabolites transferred to it from the surrounding tissues of the megasporangium and sporophyte.

(7) The sperms are brought into the vicinity of the egg directly or indirectly by means of a protuberance of the male gametophyte, called the *pollen tube.*

(8) Fertilization and development of an embryonic sporophyte regularly take place within the female gametophyte, still within the megaspore and, in turn, within the megasporangium (ovule). When the embryo within it has developed, the ovule is called a *seed*. All these correlated phenomena result in the production of seeds.

The structures and activities summarized in (1) to (8) above are, of course, only an outline of a rather complicated process, but this summary will be useful for repeated reference as we describe the details of the reproductive process in the several types of seed plants.

REPRESENTATIVE GYMNOSPERMOUS SEED PLANTS

Three types of gymnospermous seed plants are commonly seen, namely, the *cycads* (Fig. 8-8), *Ginkgo* (Fig. 8-9), and the *conifers* (Fig. 8-2). In the following paragraphs, *Pinus* (pine), a conifer, will be treated in some detail as a basis for comparison with other gymnospermous types.

Pines and Other Conifers

Pines and associated conifers form extensive forests in various parts of the world and are highly important commercially as sources of lumber and of wood pulp for the manufacture of paper and of naval stores, a general term for the products of coniferous gums or resins. Like all woody plants, the apical growth of *Pinus* is seasonal. During dormant periods, the delicate tips of the branches are covered by relatively impervious scales, thus forming *covered buds*. During the growing season, these unfold by division and elongation of the cells of the stem within the bud (Fig. 8-2). Pine leaves, familiarly known as needles, have little surface area (Fig. 8-2). Within the leaves and throughout the plant are numerous canals filled with a secretion known as resin. In most species, the needle leaves are borne in clusters on minute lateral branches of the main axes called *spur shoots* (Fig. 8-2). The stems and roots of pine contain active, vascular cambial layers that add secondary xylem, thus increasing the woodiness and diameter of the axes. The wood of pine is exceedingly homogeneous, consisting largely of conducting cells, called tracheids, and associated living parenchyma cells.

After a number of years of purely vegetative growth, young trees begin to bear spores. Unlike those of *Selaginella,* the microspores and megaspores of *Pinus* occur in separate strobili, accordingly called *microstrobili* and *megastrobili*. The microstrobili occur in subterminal clusters as the buds unfold at the beginning of the growing season, while the minute, light-green megastrobili are borne on short lateral branches of the expanding axes of terminal buds (Fig. 8-2, Me. 1). The microstrobilus is composed of an axis bearing microsporophylls, each with two elongate microsporangia on its lower surface (Fig. 8-3A). Early in the spring, the microspore mother cells (microsporocytes) produce tetrads of haploid microspores as a result of meiosis; these separate into individual microspores with inflated ("winged") cell walls (Fig. 8-3B).

The megastrobili are somewhat more complex in structure; their appendages, in part composed of megasporophylls, bear two ovules each (Fig. 8-3C). An ovule, as we saw, is a megasporangium covered with an integument (Fig. 8-4A); the passageway through the integument is known as the *micropyle*. A single megaspore mother cell in each ovule forms a row of four megaspores by meiosis; of these, the three nearest the micropyle degenerate, leaving one *functional megaspore* (Fig. 8-4B). This is approximately the same size as the microspore and lacks a thickened wall; it is intimately associated with the surrounding cells of the megasporangium, from which it no doubt draws nutriment, instead of being free from the sporangial wall as are the megaspores of *Selaginella*. With the formation, by meiosis, of microspores and megaspores, sporogenesis is complete, and the development of the sexual phase follows.

The microspores begin their internal production of male gametophytes before they are shed from the microsporangia; they are dropped when they have produced a four-celled, immature male gametophyte (Fig. 8-5A), known familiarly as a *pollen grain*.* The opening of the microsporangia releases large clouds of these sulfur-colored, dust-like pollen grains, with their contained gametophytes, which are transported great distances by air currents. At the same time in the spring when the pollen is being shed, the internodes of the axes of the megastrobili elongate slightly, thus forming fissures between successive ovule-bearing appendages. Some of the air-borne pollen grains sift into these fissures and come into contact with the tips of the ovules, which at this time have secreted a so-called *pollination droplet* through the micropyle. Upon contact with this droplet, the pollen grains float through it into the *pollen chamber* (Fig. 8-4A), a space within the apex of the megasporangium. This transfer of pollen from the microsporangium to the micropyle of the ovule is known as *pollination*. The male gametophytes complete their development within the pollen chamber and the tissues of the megasporangium, as is illustrated in the photograph in Fig. 8-6; this process takes more than a year following pollination.

During this period, the functional megaspore in each ovule initiates the development of a female gametophyte by a series of nuclear divisions and the addition of cytoplasm; the ovules and all the tissues of the megastrobilus enlarge during this process. The mature female gametophyte finally differentiates two or three *archegonia* at its micropylar pole (Fig. 8-6). The interval between pollination and maturation of the male and female gametophytes in pine is about 13 to 14 months.

* Sometimes, the term microspore is restricted to the spore before it has undergone nuclear division to form the male gametophyte; after the nucleus has divided, the microspore is called a pollen grain.

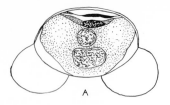
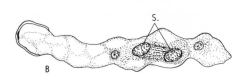

Fig. 8-5. Pine: development of the ♂ gametophyte. (A) Microspore containing immature ♂ gametophyte; (B) Mature ♂ gametophyte; note pollen tube and two sperm nuclei, s., just after division.

Meanwhile, the pollen grains, stranded on the surface of the pollen chamber by the disappearance of the pollination droplet, germinate to form pollen tubes (Figs. 8-5B and 8-6), which digest the tissues of the megasporangium as parasites and convey the sperm to the mature archegonia. Union of one of the sperm nuclei with the egg nucleus at fertilization transforms the egg nucleus of each archegonium into a zygote nucleus. The second sperm nucleus degenerates.

Fig. 8-6. Pinus virginiana. (A) l.s., upper half of ovule at fertilization (ar., archegonium with egg nucleus; ♀ g., female gametophyte; i., integument; mes., megasporangium; p.c., pollen chamber; p.t., pollen tube, or male gametophyte); (B) Fertilization, union of small male with egg nucleus.

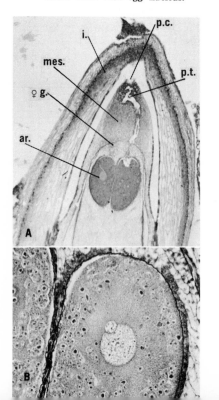

Development of embryonic sporophytes is initiated by all the fertilized zygotes, but one of the embryos outstrips the others, which abort. As the embryo develops, it grows out of the base of the archegonium (Fig. 8-7A,B) into the sterile tissues of the female gametophyte, a good deal of which it absorbs before it becomes dormant, several months after fertilization. During the development of the embryo, the cells of the integuments harden by thickening their cell walls. Similarly, soon after pollination the appendages that bear the ovules progressively enlarge (Fig. 8-2, Me. 2, Me. 3) and harden so that by the time the embryos have become dormant, the megastrobilus is extremely hard. The ovule with its embryo composes the *seed*. Strictly speaking, a seed (Fig. 8-7C) is an embryonic sporophyte, surrounded by a remnant of the female gametophyte and of the megasporangium, all of which are surrounded by the hardened integuments, now called the *seed coats*. As the seeds mature, the appendages of the megastrobilus that bear them spread apart, and the winged seeds (Fig. 8-1D,E) are shed. The embryos of those seeds that fall in suitable environments renew growth through *seed germination* (Fig. 8-7D). The embryonic leaves are called *cotyledons*.

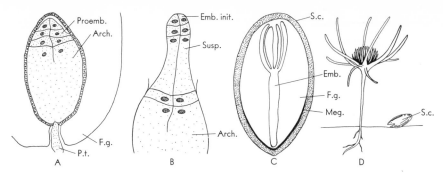

Fig. 8-7. Pine; development of embryo, seed, and germination. (A) Section of archegonium with proembryo soon after fertilization; (B) Elongation of suspensor, which pushes embryo-forming cells out of archegonium into female gametophyte; (C) m.l.s., seed; (D) Seedling (Arch., archegonium; Emb., embryo; Emb. init., embryo initial; F.g., female gametophyte; Meg., megasporangium; P.t., pollen tube; Proemb., proembryo; S.c., seed coat; Susp., suspensor).

The seed, then, is in a sense a prefabricated miniature of the mature seed plant, in this case, the pine. It develops as the result of the series of correlated morphological and physiological processes we have just summarized.

Pinus is but one of about forty genera of conifers widely distributed in both hemispheres. This group includes cedars, larches, cypresses, spruce, and firs. The reproductive process in all these plants is similar in general to that of pine, except for certain variations in detail.

The Cycads and Ginkgo

Now we shall briefly discuss, in comparative fashion, two other groups of gymnospermous seed plants. These are the *cycads* and *Ginkgo*. These plants differ from conifers more in their vegetative organs than in their reproductive process.

Fig. 8-8. Cycas revoluta, a cycad. (Courtesy Professor Elsie Quarterman.)

The cycads (Fig. 8-8), a small group of nine tropical, strobilate genera (Cycadophyta, Table 1-1), are reminiscent of the tree ferns because of their trunk-like stems and pinnately compound leaves, many of which display circinate vernation. The leaves also suggest palms, which, however, are angiosperms. Cycads are limited to the tropics and subtropics of both hemispheres. In the United States, only *Zamia* occurs natively, in Florida. In addition, the genera *Cycas* and *Dioon* are widely cultivated for their stately, palm-like foliage. The stems of cycads are mostly unbranched, slow-growing (both in height and girth), and covered by the leaf bases of preceding seasons. Although a cambium is present in the stems, its additions of secondary tissues are composed in large part of thin-walled parenchyma cells; thus, the stems are not woody. The sperm of cycads are the largest in the plant kingdom, often 300 microns * in diameter, and they can move by means of short flagella, often called cilia.

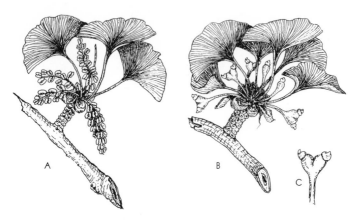

Fig. 8-9. Ginkgo biloba, **maidenhair tree: (A) Spur shoot with microstrobili; (B) Spur shoot with ovules; (C) One pair of ovules, enlarged.**

The Ginkgophyta (Table 1-1) are represented in extant flora only by the maidenhair tree, *Ginkgo biloba* (Fig. 8-9), which is a many-branched tree, like the pine and most conifers. As in pines, the clusters of leaves arise from lateral, spur shoots. The plant takes its common name from the resemblance of its thin, deciduous leaves to those of the leaflets of the maidenhair fern. The microspores occur in lax, pendulous strobili, whereas the ovules are borne in pairs at the tips of delicate stalks on different trees. The motile, ciliate sperms of *Ginkgo* are not quite as large as those of the cycads. As *Ginkgo* seeds ripen, the outer layer of the integument gets fleshy so that the seeds look like mottled plums. The fleshy layers of the mature seed may cause nausea, if smelled, and superficial skin lesions in some individuals. Although *Ginkgo* grows rapidly and is cultivated widely in the temperate zone, it seems almost to have disappeared in nature. The reasons for its near extinction are unknown. In the United States *Ginkgo* flourishes as an ornamental tree in the parks and on the streets of many cities, among others New York and Washington, D.C.

In conclusion, we should emphasize that the gymnosperms are quite diverse vegetatively, although all possess a generally similar pattern of reproduction in which the manner of production of seeds is especially distinctive in differentiating them from angiosperms. As compared with angiosperms, gymnosperms are decidedly a minority in our present flora.

* One micron equals 0.001 mm, or 1/25,000 of an inch.

The Flowering
Plants,
or Angiosperms

CHAPTER NINE

The second great group of seed-producing plants, the angiosperms (Table 1-1), is both the largest in numbers of genera,
species, and individuals and also the most recent group of
plants to develop on the earth (Fig. 6-1). The angiosperms,
commonly known as flowering plants, differ from gymnospermous seed plants in, among other respects, that their
ovules and seeds are enclosed *within* the pistil,* or megasporophyll (Fig. 8-1A–C), which later becomes a seed-bearing *fruit.* The structure of the pistil in certain primitive angiosperms suggests that the enclosure of the seeds may have
come about by the evolutionary folding of a leaf-like, ovule-
bearing megasporophyll.

The angiosperms exceed all other vascular plants in range
of diversity of the plant body and habitat, and in their utility
to mankind. Both woody and herbaceous angiosperms exist,
and among the latter, especially, there is considerable varia-

* A simple pistil is composed of one ovule-bearing megasporophyll,
or *carpel;* the carpel, therefore, is the equivalent of one megasporophyll. Compound pistils are composed of several simple pistils (or
carpels or megasporophylls) that have become united during evolution and may do so also in development.

tion of vegetative structure, including such diverse types as bulbous hyacinths, onions and lilies, and rhizomatous *Iris* and many grasses. Examples of diversity in habitat are aquatic water lilies, *Elodea,* and *Lemna,* or duckweed (Fig. 5-1), and such xeric genera as cacti. In the latter, the leaves are much reduced or absent in mature individuals. Woody species are used extensively as lumber and fuel and as the source of commercial cork, while herbaceous types are important sources of food, textiles, drugs, and vegetable oils. Both the vegetative and reproductive portions of angiosperms are used as foods. Sweet potatoes, carrots, turnips, beets, and parsnips are examples of fleshy roots that are important foods; white, or "Irish," potatoes and asparagus are stems. Various greens, such as spinach, turnips, beets, and lettuce are leaves. Cabbages and head lettuce are immense terminal buds, whereas the fleshy petioles of rhubarb and celery are also foodstuffs.

Of the reproductive organs of angiosperms, examples of flowers, fruits, and seeds used as food are even more abundant. In both cauliflower and broccoli, we eat groups of flowers, called *inflorescences.* National cultures and economies are based on the use for food of such fruits as grains of corn, rice, wheat, and rye. Indeed, fruits used as food are too numerous to list completely, but among them we may cite citrus fruits, squashes and melons, tomatoes, grapes, bananas, apples, pears, and various berries. The preceding list contains examples, such as tomatoes and squash, of fruits that the laymen frequently classify as "vegetables." Botanically, structures are fruits if they are derived, at least in part, from the pistil, or megasporophylls of the flower; vegetative organs and vegetables, strictly speaking, are nonreproductive parts of plants, but the term vegetable, in common parlance, is loosely used.

THE GROSS MORPHOLOGY OF FLOWERS

The *flower* is the organ of reproduction of the angiosperms, but it is a difficult structure to define in precise enough terms to distinguish it from aggregations of microsporophylls and megasporophylls which we called strobili, or cones, in gymnosperms. A generalized flower is illustrated in Fig. 9-1, and the parts mentioned in the following discussion may be located in this figure and in Fig. 9-2. Flowers, like strobili, are stems in which the apical meristems have differentiated completely, so that the meristem, in a sense, is "used up." In flowers, as in strobili, the axis, or *receptacle,* that bears the sporophylls has short internodes, so that the sporophylls are borne either in a tight spiral arrangement or in one that is whorled and cyclic. In the latter case, three to five sporophylls usually arise at a given level of the axis. Floral axes usually bear sterile appendages in addition to the sporophylls; these are *sepals* (collectively, the *calyx*), generally green but sometimes other colors or white, and *petals* (collectively, the *corolla*). Petals may be colored or white. Sepals and petals are not

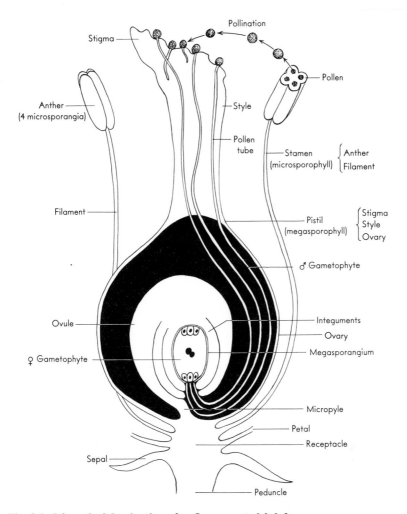

Fig. 9-1. Schematized longisection of a flower, parts labeled.

essential to the reproductive process and may be greatly modified or even absent. The essential parts of the flower are the *sporophylls* themselves. In angiosperms, the microsporophylls are known as *stamens* and the megasporophylls, or fused groups of them, as *pistils*. Stamens produce microspores, and pistils produce megaspores. Stamens and pistils of angiosperms probably correspond, respectively, to the microsporophylls and megasporophylls of gymnosperms; this correspondence will facilitate our understanding of the reproductive process in angiosperms, to be described below.

Pistils (Figs. 9-1, 9-2, and 9-11) usually consist of an enlarged basal portion, the *ovary*, which contains one or more ovules and a receptive surface for pollen, the *stigma*. The stigma and ovary are connected by a more or less elongated *style*. Pistils may be either simple or compound. Simple pistils (Figs. 8-1B and 9-1) usually have but one cavity containing ovules,

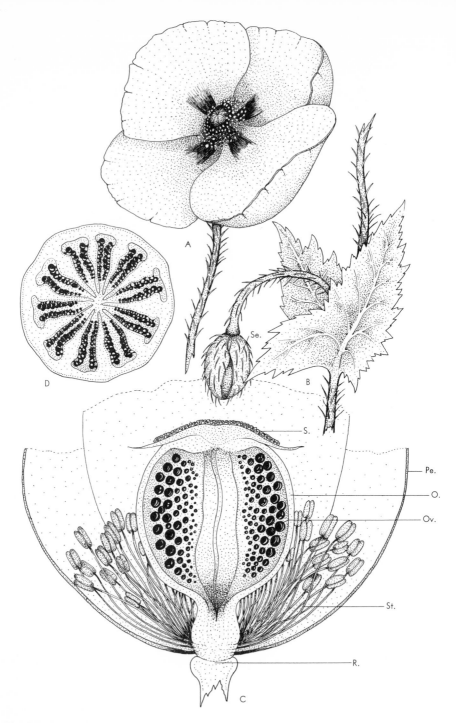

Fig. 9-2. Poppy, floral structure. (A) Open flower; (B) Flower in bud stage showing two sepals (se.) which are shed as the flower opens; (C) Longitudinal bisection of flower (enlarged): O., ovary; Ov., ovule; Pe., petal; R., receptacle; S., stigma; St., stamens or microsporophylls; (D) Transection of compound ovary (enlarged) consisting of 10 carpels.

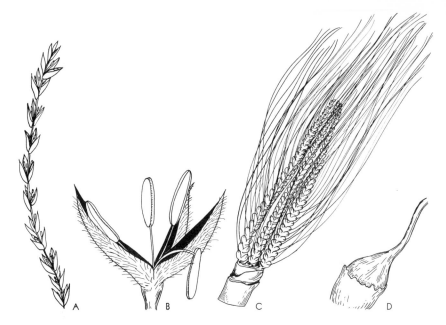

Fig. 9-3. Flowers of corn. (A) Portion of staminate inflorescence; (B) Single staminate flower; (C) Pistillate inflorescence or young "ear" of corn; (D) Single pistillate flower with stigma-style.

whereas many compound pistils have ovaries partitioned into two or more chambers (Figs. 8-1C and 9-11B).*

In the vast majority of angiosperms both stamens and pistils occur on the same individual sporophyte and are usually together in a given flower. In some species, however, *staminate flowers* bear microsporophylls alone, while others, the *pistillate flowers,* have only megasporophylls on their receptacles. Such staminate and pistillate flowers are said to be imperfect. Corn is a good example of a plant with imperfect flowers; these are briefly described in the legend to Fig. 9-3.

In a few other angiosperms, the staminate and pistillate flowers are borne by different individuals, as in the willow, poplar (cottonwood), and mulberry, among others (Fig. 9-4).

Flowers may be large and conspicuous and borne singly, or they may occur together in various types of inflorescences in which the individual flowers are smaller and less striking. Of the various types of inflorescences, the head, or *capitulum* (Fig. 9-5), is especially frequent. In the capitulum, like that illustrated in Fig. 9-5A, two types of flowers are present, the minute, bell-like, central *disc* flowers (Fig. 9-5B) and the larger, peripheral ray flowers (Fig. 9-5C). The disc flowers are perfect and complete, calyx, corolla, stamens, and pistil being present. In the ray flowers, the corolla is split open near the base, and stamens are absent.

* However, some compound pistils, like those in the grass, sedge, and composite families, have only one chamber, partitions between the fused parts being absent.

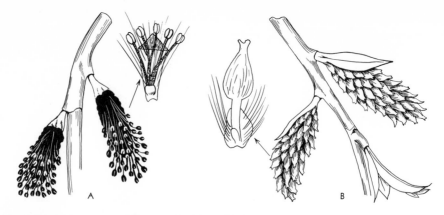

Fig. 9-4. Inflorescences and flowers of willow. (A) Staminate, with single stami-nate flower enlarged, above right; (B) Pistillate, with single pistillate flower en-larged, above left.

THE REPRODUCTIVE PROCESS IN ANGIOSPERMS

To anyone who has mastered the essential features of reproduction in gymnosperms described in the preceding chapter, the reproductive process in angiosperms will not seem unduly complicated. Attempts to abbreviate an account of this process, however, may result in inaccuracies and confusion, so we shall present it in some detail. The process consists of the following phenomena: (1) sporogenesis; (2) development of the gameto-phytes and gametogenesis; (3) pollination; (4) fertilization; and (5) embryogeny and development of the seed and fruit.

Sporogenesis

The production of flowers with their sporophylls signals the maturation of the angiosperm sporophyte. In all annuals and many perennials, the flowers, seed, and fruit are produced during the first growing season, but in many perennials, a number of years of purely vegetative growth precede the appearance of flowers.

Microsporogenesis does not differ in any important way in angiosperms and gymnosperms. Microspores are produced in groups of four from microsporocytes (microspore mother cells) that undergo meiosis within the microsporangia of the stamen (Figs. 9-6 and 9-7). The microsporangia are collectively called the *anther;* the stalk that elevates them is the *filament.* Like the microspores and pollen grains of gymnosperms, those of angio-sperms have walls that are variously sculptured and ornamented in ways that are highly characteristic of a given species; this marking may be quite elaborate (Fig. 9-7D). In any case, the spores of plants can be identified and assigned with great accuracy to their species; this, in part, is the division of botany known as *palynology.* Identification of pollen grains is important in the diagnosis and treatment of such allergies as hay fever, rose fever, etc.

Megasporogenesis in flowering plants is like that in gymnosperms. You will recall that the megasporangia of seed plants are permanently enclosed in integuments and that they are called ovules (Fig. 9-8A,B). Recall too that in gymnosperms, the ovules are produced *on the surface* of appendages of strobili (most cycads, conifers) (Fig. 8-1D,E) or at the ends of stalks (*Ginkgo*) (Fig. 8-9). In the angiosperms, the ovules always occur within the more or less inflated base of the megasporophyll known as the ovary (see Figs. 8-1A–C and 9-11). The number of ovules within a given ovary may vary from one to many, and their place of attachment is also variable. The remainder of the megasporophyll is composed of the style and stigma (Figs. 9-1, 9-2, and 9-11A), the latter being a specialized surface to which the pollen grains adhere at pollination. As in the gymnosperms, each ovule usually produces but a single megasporocyte (megaspore mother cell); this undergoes meiosis to form a linear tetrad of megaspores (Fig. 9-8B) while the flower is in the bud stage. In angiosperms, also, only a single functional megaspore survives (Fig. 9-8C). Megasporogenesis in angiosperms is not essentially different from that in gymnosperms. It occurs during the bud stage of the flower.

Fig. 9-5. Helianthus sp. (A) Capitulum, or inflorescence; (B) Detail of disc flower; (C) Detail of ray flower (corolla only partially shown).

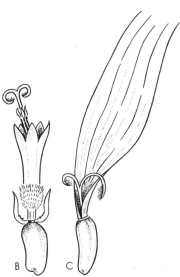

Development of the Gametophytes and Gametogenesis

Compared with the time required for the development of the gametophytes in many gymnosperms, the process in most angiosperms is rapid. This indicates that the gametophytes themselves are far less complex. As usual in seed plants, the development of the male gametophyte from the microspore is at first intrasporal and is initiated soon after microsporogenesis has been completed (Fig. 9-9A). Except for the formation of the pollen tube following pollination, development of the male gametophyte may be completed within the microspore wall before the pollen has been shed from the anther. In some species, on the other hand, the nuclear division that produces the two sperm nuclei occurs in the pollen tube during germination. The mature male gametophyte (Figs. 9-6B and 9-9) contains only three nuclei—the tube nucleus—and the two sperms; the latter probably are surrounded by delicate sheaths of specialized cytoplasm delimited from that of the pollen tube.

In most angiosperms, the nucleus of the functional megaspore undergoes three successive divisions to form eight haploid nuclei which become somewhat differentiated and characteristically arranged within the functional megaspore, now transformed into a mature female gametophyte (Figs. 9-1, 9-6, and 9-9C,D). Of the three nuclei nearest the micropylar pole of the female gametophyte, one functions as the *egg nucleus* and the other two are known as *synergids*. These are delimited from the common cyto-

Fig. 9-6. Summary of the reproductive process in angiosperms. (A) Lower portion of an anther (four microsporangia); (B) Microsporocyte; (C) Tetrad of microspores; (D) Mature microspores; (E) Median longitudinal section (m.l.s.) of an ovule containing a megasporocyte; (F) Megasporocyte enlarged; (G) Linear tetrad of megaspores; (H) Functional and 3 degenerating megaspores; (I–J) Maturation of male gametophyte and formation of pollen tube; (K) Mature female gametophyte developed by functional megaspore; (L) m.l.s. of an ovule at moment of double fertilization; (M) m.l.s. of an ovule soon after fertilization; (N) Dormant seed with dicotyledonous embryo (A., antipodal cells; E., egg cell; Emb., embryo; End., endosperm; F.g., female gametophyte; G.c., generative cell; I., integuments; M., micropyle; Meg., megasporangium; P.n., polar nuclei; S., synergids; S.c., seed coats; Sp., sperm cells; T.c., tube cell; T.n., tube nucleus).

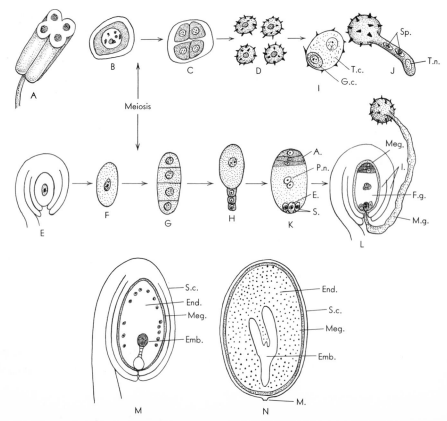

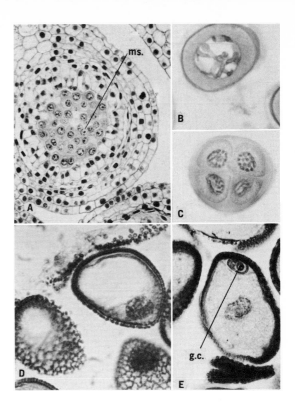

Fig. 9-7. Lily (Lilium). (A) Transection, anther lobe or microsporangium (ms., microsporocytes); (B) Microsporocyte, prophase of meiosis; (C) Tetrad of microspores; (D) Microspore with sculptured wall; (E) Pollen grain containing immature male gametophyte consisting of large tube cell and generative cell; g.c.

plasm by delicate membranes. At the opposite pole, three *antipodal cells* are formed. The two nuclei that previously migrated from the poles to the center of the female gametophyte are, because of their migration, called *polar nuclei*. Compared with that of most gymnosperms, the female gametophyte of angiosperms has a short existence and little internal differentiation. A female sex organ, or archegonium, is absent and represented only by an egg cell. As the flower opens, then, and as the stigmas become receptive, the ovule or ovules within the ovary contain mature or maturing female gametophytes. Angiosperm gametophytes, like those of gymnosperms, are parasitic on the sporophyte.

Pollination and Fertilization

At the same time, the microsporangia, often called "pollen sacs" in angiosperms, open by fissures or pores and begin to shed the pollen grains with their enclosed male gametophytes. Some of these are transferred by various forces such as gravity, wind, insects, or other animals or even by water (in certain aquatics), to the receptive surface of the stigma (Fig. 9-1). A number of special relationships between insects and the pollination of flowers are well known and indicative of closely correlated evolution of the flowering plants and insects involved. Thus, pollination of the female inflorescence of figs, which results in the edible fruit, is accomplished by a small wasp, *Blastophaga;* and when these wasps are absent, edible fruits do not develop. Long-tongued insects, such as certain bees,

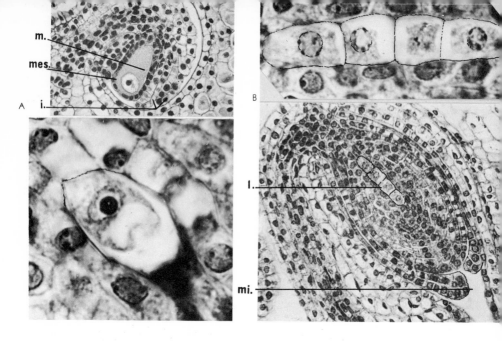

Fig. 9-8. (A) m.l.s. of young ovule of lily (Lilium) (i., integuments; m., mega-sporocyte; mes., megasporangium); (B) L.s., ovule of Oenothera with linear tetrad of megaspores, l., enlarged above (mi., micropyle); (C) Functional and degenerated megaspores of Oenothera.

wasps, and butterflies, in search of nectar (which may contain up to 25% glucose) and pollen are the agents of pollination in many plants. One of the most interesting examples of a seemingly obligate relationship is that between the Spanish bayonet, *Yucca,* and the yucca moth, *Pronuba.* The latter lays its eggs in the ovary of the *Yucca* flower and immediately there-after places a ball of pollen it has gathered on the stigma of the *Yucca* flower. The larvae developing from the eggs eat a few of the seeds, but large numbers of seeds survive to maintain *Yucca* plants.

In the process of pollination, a second great difference between angio-spermous and gymnospermous seed plants is apparent. In angiosperms, pollination is the transfer of pollen grains from the microsporangia of the stamen, not directly to the micropyle of the ovule as in gymnosperms, but to the stigma of the megasporophyll. Once on the stigma surface, the pollen grains germinate rapidly to form pollen tubes, which penetrate the tissues of the stigma and style and enter the ovary. If pollination has been sufficiently heavy, a pollen tube grows toward the micropyle of each ovule, enters it, and makes contact with the female gametophyte. Prob-ably because of differences in turgor pressure, the pollen tubes burst and discharge their nuclei into the cytoplasm of that gametophyte on contact.

At this point, a third important difference between angiosperms and gymnosperms becomes apparent, namely, the occurrence of *double fertiliza-tion,* a phenomenon known only in flowering plants. This involves the union of one sperm nucleus with the egg nucleus and of the other sperm nucleus with the two polar nuclei * to form a triploid nucleus (Fig. 9-9D). The activity of both sperms in these phenomena suggested the term "double fertilization." Here again, although accompanied by a number of attendant secondary phenomena, we see that sexual reproduction involves the union of cells and nuclei and the association of chromosomes—in this case to form both a zygote and a triploid nucleus called the *primary endosperm nucleus.* In the postfertilization processes, now to be considered, these two nuclei play stellar roles.

Embryogeny and the Development of the Seed and Fruit

The occurrence of pollination and double fertilization stimulates nuclear and cell division in the ovule and pistil (and often of such closely associated structures as the receptacle); accordingly, these enlarge. The stamens and petals gradually disintegrate or are shed. These changes even-

---

* These may unite with each other before fertilization.

Fig. 9-9. The gametophytic phase in flowering plants. (A) Immature male gametophyte within pollen grain consisting of generative cell and tube cell; (B) Pollen germination and mature male gametophyte; (C) Median longitudinal section of ovule with mature female gametophyte; (D) Double fertilization in lily (A., antipodal cells; E., egg; E.n., egg nucleus; F.g., female gametophyte; G.c., generative cell; I., integument; M., micropyle; Me., megasporangium; P.n., polar nuclei; S., synergid; Sp., sperm cell; Sp.-1, sperm nucleus 1; Sp.-2, sperm nucleus 2).

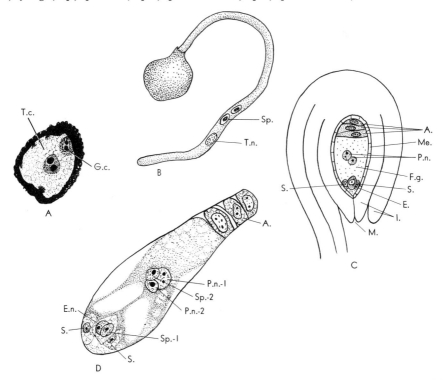

tually become noticeable to the unaided eye as the ovary enlarges to form the fruit and the ovules to form the seeds. Soon after double fertilization, the primary endosperm nucleus initiates a series of nuclear divisions to form triploid endosperm nuclei (Fig. 9-10A), which, in most cases, are sooner or later separated from one another by cell walls to form a cellular endosperm. This tissue is rich in stored metabolites that are transported there from the parent sporophyte, and it serves as a source of nutrition for the developing embryo. Thus we have a fourth difference between angiosperms and gymnosperms: In angiosperms, the embryonic sporophyte is nourished by a special nutritive tissue, the *endosperm,* which is formed *after* fertilization. You will recall that the gymnosperm embryo obtains its metabolites from the vegetative tissues of the female gametophyte (Fig. 8-7B,C).

Sometime after the initiation of endosperm development, the zygote, by a series of nuclear and cell divisions, forms a mass of cells which varies in extent and degree of organization among the

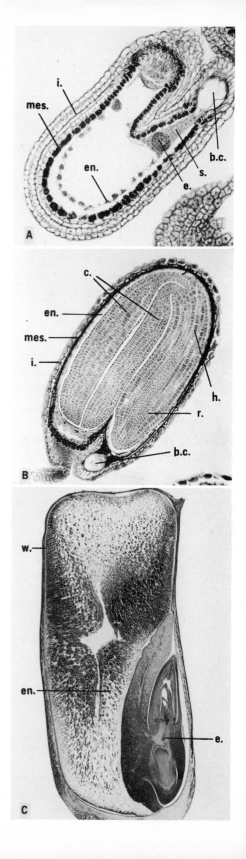

Fig. 9-10. Embryogeny of flowering plants. (A,B) Capsella, shepherd's purse; (C) Zea mays, corn. (e., embryo; en., endosperm; i., integument; b.c., basal cell; c., cotyledons; h., hypocotyl; mes., megasporangium; r., radicle, or embryonic root; s., suspensor, w., seed coats and ovary wall.) (C, reproduced by permission from *Botanical Microtechnique,* 3rd ed., by J. E. Sass, published by the Iowa State University Press.)

genera of flowering plants. This mass of cells is the young embryonic sporophyte of the next generation, the so-called *germ* of the seed. In a few angiosperms, like orchids, the embryo enters a period of dormancy after only a few cells have developed. In most others, the embryo consists of an axis, the *hypocotyl,* bearing one or two *cotyledons;* between them (in dicotyledons) is a terminal bud, the *plumule,* or *epicotyl,* and below is an embryonic root, the *radicle* (Fig. 9-10B,C). As the development of the embryo nears completion, the tissues of the ovule become dehydrated, and the integuments become dark in color and impervious; by this time, the ovules have matured into seeds. As Fig. 9-10B,C illustrates, a seed consists of an embryonic sporophyte ("germ") in a dormant condition; this is embedded within the endosperm and remaining megasporangial–tissues and integuments, the last now being called seed coats. In some angiosperms, the embryo does not become dormant until it has digested most of the endosperm; as a result, the embryo is massive, having, in fact, absorbed into itself (usually in the fleshy cotyledons) the metabolites stored in the endosperm. Beans, peas, peanuts, and many other leguminous plants have seeds of this type.

In addition to enlargement, the ovary of the flower, and in some cases associated structures, may undergo considerable change in shape and differentiation of tissues during embryogeny. This is clear in such a familiar example as the tomato (Figs. 8-1C and 9-11), in which the ovary in the flower bud is a minute, rather firm, whitish-green structure composed

Fig. 9-11. Structure of the tomato pistil. (A) Flower just after pollination. With petals and stamens, and with one sepal removed; (B) Transection of ovary, somewhat enlarged (L., locule; O., ovary; Ov., ovule; P., peduncle; S., sepal; Sti., stigma; Sty., style).

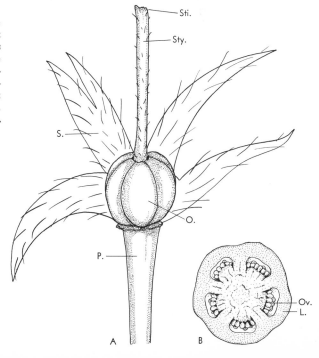

largely of meristematic cells and of some vascular tissues. After fertilization, the ovary enlarges tremendously, passing through the familiar "green tomato" stage until it finally ripens. In the latter process, the green plastids become yellow-orange, and complex cellular changes occur to form the skin-like, firm, fleshy, and juicy layers of the fully ripened fruit. Different changes occur in fruit formation in other angiosperms and with various modifications give rise to the great diversity of fruits characteristic of that group.

Fig. 9-12. Seeds and seedlings. (A) Corn (Zea mays): **(1) ungerminated grain; (2) early germination; (3) six-day-old seedling; (B) Garden pea** (Pisum sativum); **(1) seed covered with seed coats; embryonic root barley visible; (2) seed coat removed showing two fleshy cotyledons and embryonic root; (3) hemisected seed; (4) eight-day-old seedling (C., cotyledon; E., epicotyl; L., leaf; P.r., primary root; R., radicle; S.l., soil line; S.c., seed coat).**

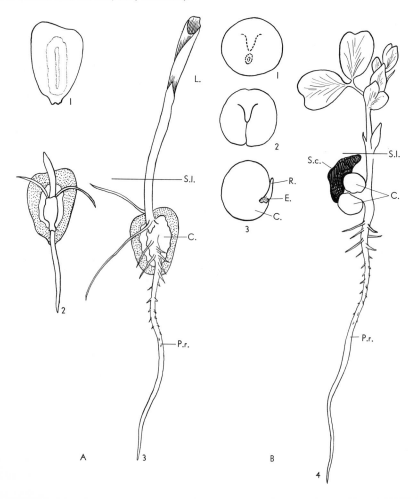

As the seed and fruit mature in various plants, the seeds may either be ejected by the opening of the drying fruits, or they may be freed only after the fleshy and stony layers of the enclosing fruits have rotted. If they are planted or if they chance to come to rest in a suitable environment, they sooner or later germinate (Fig. 9-12). Germination is merely a continuation of embryogenesis, with the emergence of the embryonic sporophyte into an external environment.

Various types of seed dormancy occur among angiosperms. These may be morphological, as in the case of the rudimentary embryos alluded to previously, or physiological, involving changes in permeability of seed coats, activation of enzymes, etc. In general, seeds germinate when in the presence of adequate moisture and oxygen and within a given range of temperatures, which varies with the species. Light too is necessary for seed germination in some species, lettuce being a well-known example. The emergence of the radicle and of the other embryonic organs, the formation of additional leaves, and the increase in axis length sooner or later establish the embryonic sporophyte as an independent organism, and the remains of the seed disintegrate.

Reproduction in angiosperms, then, although similar in many ways to that of gymnosperms, differs in these important respects: (1) The ovules and hence the seeds are borne *within* megasporophylls instead of being exposed on their surfaces; this is *angiospermy,* as contrasted with *gymnospermy* (Fig. 8-1); (2) development of the gametophytes is a much more abbreviated process in angiosperms than it is in gymnosperms; (3) the gametophytes themselves are simpler in angiosperms; (4) pollination in angiosperms involves the transfer of pollen grains from the microsporangia (anther) to the receptive surface of the megasporophyll (stigma), rather than to the micropyle of the ovule, as is the case in gymnosperms; (5) double fertilization occurs only in angiosperms; (6) the embryo of angiosperms is nourished by endosperm, a special tissue which arises *after* fertilization, rather than by the female gametophyte as it is in gymnosperms; (7) the seeds of angiosperms are enclosed within fruits, which are enlarged megasporophylls (pistils) sometimes with associated parts of the flower; fruits of this type are absent in gymnosperms in which the megasporophyll does not enclose the seed.

Summary

CHAPTER TEN

It now seems appropriate to consider the various types of organisms we have described in some detail, for the purpose of consolidating our understanding of the plants themselves and the groups they represent, and to emphasize some of the important principles they illustrate. We are now in a better position than we were at the outset to consider the diversity of the plant kingdom, the causes for the diversity, and the problems of relationship and classification of plants. Let us begin by summarizing some of the more important phenomena described in the preceding chapters.

ORGANIZATION OF THE PLANT BODY

Our discussion of the diversity of the plant kingdom has included reference to such groups of organisms as algae, fungi, mosses and liverworts, seedless vascular plants (psilophytes, club mosses, arthrophytes, and ferns), and seed-bearing vascular plants, including gymnosperms and angiosperms. Was there any important reason for studying them in that particular order? Could we have started as well at the other end of the series, or, perhaps with any intermediate group, and have proceeded in a different order? The order of study is indeed significant for it reflects increasing complexity. There is evidence that this increasing complexity was built up over many millions of years, starting from relative simplicity. Diversities of structure and function, both vegetative and reproductive, are best explained as manifestations of gradual change, or evolution. We must be cautious, however, in our appraisal of supposed simplicity and complexity. In the first place, *apparent* simplicity, as, for example, that in the many aquatic plants which have little differentiated xylem, may well be a *secondary* simplicity through loss of complexity, a phenomenon known as *reduction*. The absence of xylem and phloem * from algae, liverworts, and mosses, on the other hand, is usually interpreted as true simplicity and as a *primitive* condition.

Some further words of caution are appropriate here. In spite of their manifest complexity, the so-called "higher plants" are performing essentially the same biological functions that go on even in unicellular organisms, which are often spoken of as the "lower" or "simple" plants. These manifold chemical and physical processes are elegantly complex and correlated in all living organisms, so that the terms "higher" and "lower," "simple" and "complex," are often misleading and illusory. The terms "alternate" or "different," or "ancient," "less ancient," and "recent," or "similar" and "dissimilar" might more appropriately be used in some of these comparisons.

On the other hand, when you consider unicellular, colonial, and multicellular organisms, it is clear that an organism is more than the sum of its individual cells. This is evidenced by the movement through the plant body of organizing substances that evoke differential responses from descendants of the initial reproductive cell, usually the zygote. The evidence of modern electron microscopy shows clearly that multicellular plants are not made of isolated cells stacked together like bricks or boxes. An extensive, net-like system of protoplasm passes through the walls from cell to cell, so the original unity of the zygote probably is partially preserved as it gives rise to the multicellular organism. Furthermore, development of the multicellular organism involves correlated responses to the environment. Multicellular plants and animals are considered by some biologists to be *cell republics* that have evolved from the aggregation of one-celled organisms. Others look upon one-celled organisms as being complex and acellular, not strictly comparable to single tissue cells. These theorists regard multicellular organisms as having arisen by secondary subdivision of the organisms into cells.

Since all organisms start as single cells, *ontogeny* (the development of individual organisms) suggests that multicellular organisms probably arose by the failure of cells to separate after the completion of cell division. Growth in multicellular plants may be generalized, but in most it is restricted to the tips of stems and roots or to certain definite other regions.

* Phloem-like cells occur in certain brown algae, the kelps (see page 17).

Apical growth is the rule in a number of algae, fungi, and in all the remaining types of plants, although in many plants lateral growth is also pronounced. Some exceptions occur in members of the grass family in which intercalary meristems also are present. A survey of the plant kingdom indicates that the size of organisms in which the component cells are essentially uniform, as in the sea lettuce, *Ulva* (Fig. 2-1G), and a number of other algae and liverworts, is limited, especially when the plants are not aquatic. Although internal differentiation is apparent to a limited degree in algae, in the form of holdfasts and rhizoids, and to a greater degree in such algae as the kelps, in which phloem-like tissues are present, the stimulus for internal complexity seems to have been the land habitat. This is apparent in some measure in such liverworts as *Riccia* (Fig. 4-7A), in the stems and leaves of certain mosses, and, finally, to the greatest degree in the vascular plants.

In the vascular plants, with the exception of the Psilophyta, the plant body consists of an axis composed of stem, root, and leaves. Of the latter there are two fundamentally different types. Of these, microphyllous leaves (with simple unbranched veins) characterize only the Microphyllophyta (*Selaginella,* etc.) and *Equisetum,* while the remaining vascular plants are macrophyllous. It has been suggested that macrophyllous leaves represent branching axes that have become flattened and blade-like through extension of the nonvascular tissues by a sort of webbing.

REPRODUCTION

We have alluded in earlier chapters to various methods for propagation— both asexual and sexual, the latter involving cellular and nuclear union and associations of parental chromosomes. The simplest and most direct method of asexual reproduction is by *fragmentation* of a plant itself. This is exemplified by binary fission (cell division) in unicellular organisms, as well as by various cases in which fragments of a plant regenerate complete new individuals. Examples of this are the dissociation of such colonial algae as *Pandorina,* and of such truly multicellular organisms as branching liverworts, mosses, fern and other rhizomes, and by leaf, stem, and root cuttings. Special agents of reproduction (unicellular and multicellular spores of various kinds, such as air-borne spores of fungi, liverworts, mosses, and ferns, and zoospores of certain algae and fungi) are also produced. All of these are asexual in that they develop into new plants individually without uniting with another spore.

Sexual reproduction throughout the plant kingdom almost always involves a union of cells and always a union of nuclei, and, accordingly, the association of chromosomes and, ultimately, meiosis. The origin of sexual reproduction remains unknown, but evidence in unicellular algae (page 16) suggests that it resulted from inadequate supplies of certain metabolites.

Less complex organisms, such as unicellular algae and fungi, are only *apparently* and deceptively simple, for they harbor both vegetative or somatic and reproductive functions. The gamete of *Chlamydomonas* (p. 13) is merely an immature individual that is sexually active and capable of union with another compatible individual as a result of certain chemical changes within it and on its surface. In certain colonial and filamentous algae and fungi, and in all plants in other groups, the vegetative function is more clearly segregated from the reproductive, as is indicated by the formation of special fertile areas containing reproductive cells, often in gametangia and sporangia. The gametes of *Chlamydomonas,* on the contrary, are both vegetative and reproductive in function and are primitive in this respect. This is evidenced by the fact that gametes which fail to unite will, under suitable conditions, produce large populations by cell division. In multicellular organisms, these powers of rejuvenation and asexual reproduction, in most cases, no longer characterize the differentiated reproductive cells, and those that do not unite die.

From the preceding chapters, it is clear that, with respect to the distribution of the compatible gametes ($+$ and $-$, male and female), plants may be either *homothallic* (bisexual or hermaphroditic) or *heterothallic* (unisexual). Certain species of *Chlamydomonas* and *Volvox,* of mosses, and the gametophytes of *Psilotum, Lycopodium, Equisetum,* and those of many ferns all exemplify homothallism. On the contrary, other species of *Chlamydomonas, Pandorina, Volvox, Achlya ambisexualis, Rhizopus, Polytrichum,* and the gametophytes of *Selaginella* and all the seed plants are heterothallic.

It should also be apparent that gametes may or may not be differentiated morphologically. Thus, we have seen that among the algae and fungi, various degrees of gametic differentiation exist, from morphological isogamy (*Chlamydomonas moewusii, Rhizopus*) through heterogamy (*Chlamydomonas* spp.), culminating in oogamy. The last-named condition, in which the minute male gametes are called *sperms* and the large female gametes *eggs,* occurs in some algae (*Volvox, Fucus*) and fungi (*Achlya*) and universally in liverworts, mosses, and vascular plants. It should be evident that in defining isogamy as the condition that produces undifferentiated gametes, we are saying that the lack of difference between uniting gametes is more apparent than real. From ingenious genetical and biochemical experiments, it is clear that even isogametes are physiologically and chemically different from each other, and these differences are apparently the basis for the compatible union in which zygotes are formed.

From a survey of the various reproductive phenomena in the plant kingdom, we may arrive at a number of generalizations, among them the following:

(1) An individual plant may be haploid, with a single, basic complement of chromosomes in its nuclei, throughout its existence. The diploid condition prevails only temporarily in the zygote of such species, which at

germination divides meiotically to form a new generation of haploid individuals. This occurs only among algae and fungi and is exemplified by *Chlamydomonas, Rhizopus,* and *Achlya,* among others.

(2) In a few algae (*Fucus,* for one), quite the opposite is true, for the individual plant is diploid throughout its existence and only its gametes, which arise by meiosis, are haploid. Their union to form a zygote initiates a new diploid individual.

(3) Certain algae (*Ulva,* the sea lettuce, for example) and fungi, and all the liverworts, mosses and vascular plants (therefore, the great majority of plants) possess *both* haploid and diploid phases in those phases designated as gametophytic and sporophytic, respectively. These alternate in regular sequence, so that the haploid, sexual gametophyte forms gametes that unite to produce zygotes which, in turn, give rise to diploid sporophytes that produce asexual spores, as a result of meiosis. The sporophytes and gametophytes may be physically connected: sporophyte upon gametophyte (in mosses); or gametophyte upon sporophyte (in seed plants); or independent of each other (as in the fern). In the liverworts and mosses, the gametophytic phase is dominant in duration and stature, whereas in vascular plants the sporophyte is dominant and the gametophyte ephemeral. This last sentence should not be construed to mean that there is a sort of antagonism between sporophyte and gametophyte. Both are merely different phases of the same organism. Inasmuch as meiosis, with its reassortment of parental genes, is the culmination of sexual reproduction, spores are "asexual" only in the sense that they undergo further development without union with each other. Actually, since they are products of meiosis, they themselves are an ultimate result of sexual union.

Finally, the land plants may be divided into those that are homosporous (producing similar spores) and those that are heterosporous (with dimorphic spores). The most pronounced type of heterospory we have discussed is present in *Selaginella,* in some species of which the megaspores are hundreds of times larger than microspores. The inevitable result of heterospory, it will be recalled, is the production of heterothallic gametophytes (although these sometimes arise from homosporous spores, as in *Polytrichum*). The seed plants are usually interpreted as being heterosporous, the similar size of microspores and megaspores being regarded as the result of the permanent retention of the megaspore within the megasporangium.

The seed is apparently a highly efficient mechanism for perpetuating and disseminating the species. Furthermore, the habit of producing seeds must account in part for the dominance of the angiosperms in our present flora.

DEVELOPMENT OF PLANTS IN TIME; CLASSIFICATION

In Chapter 1, we stated that current classifications of the plant kingdom are natural, or phylogenetic, in that they attempt to group organisms in categories that indicate real, genetic relationships. Now that we have surveyed representative types of plants, we can discuss the possible relationships of currently living plant groups to one another and to extinct members of the plant kingdom, the latter known to us only as fossils. Phylogenetic systems of classification, as indicative of real relationships of higher taxa such as families, orders, classes, and divisions, are speculative, necessarily the more so, the higher the category. This is in contrast to evidences of evolutionary change in individuals and species where experimental procedure is possible. Thus, X-rays, chemicals such as nitrogen mustard gas, and other agents produce changes or *mutations* in individuals that may be transmitted to their offspring, a direct and incontrovertible evidence of change and relationship by descent. The occurrence of such mutations in nature and their segregation and recombination in sexual reproduction are undoubtedly responsible for changes in individuals, populations, and species. These changes are effected by natural selection of mutations.

From such evidence, we assume that the operation of mutation and natural selection over millions of years has brought about the diversity now apparent in our flora and fauna. No experimental evidence is available to confirm relationships among plants of the past and their supposed descendants now living. Recent identification of amino acids from fossil material, however, suggests that comparative chemical analyses of fossils might well contribute to our knowledge of relationships. The evidences that support speculations regarding the origin and putative relationships among the groups of plants, in our present flora and those of the past, reside in comparative morphology of living plants, their geographical distribution, their comparative biochemistry, and the study of extinct plants as revealed in the fossil record. A few examples of these several lines of evidence will be presented in the following paragraphs.

The comparative study of plants (and animals) reveals certain common attributes cited previously in Chapter 1. Among these are similarity in cellular organization, metabolism, reproductive phenomena (including sexuality, meiosis, and life cycles), inheritance, and the capacity for adaptation. The occurrence of the same active, photosynthetic pigment, chlorophyll *a,* throughout the plant kingdom (except in fungi) and of the storage product, starch, in a great majority of green plants, are examples of significant, common attributes. The production of archegonia, in liverworts, mosses, seedless vascular plants, cycads, and conifers is another example of a widely distributed characteristic. In a word, there are a number of attributes common to species, to genera, families, orders, classes, and, finally, to divisions of plants—both living and fossil—which indicate continuity. These are most satisfactorily explained on the basis of kinship.

The fossil record presents us with important information regarding the course of evolution and the relationship of various forms of plant life. As the original, igneous rocks of the earth's crust weathered, particles were washed away and deposited as sediments in bodies of water. Among these particles, various organic remains were deposited. Later, when compression transformed these mixed sediments into rocks, the organic remains sometimes were preserved as fossils. These are of various types and differ in the perfection of their preservation. The most perfectly preserved are *petrifactions* (fossils in which the plant remains themselves are embedded in a rocky matrix), in which details of microscopic structure are remarkably clear upon sectioning.

The older strata of sedimentary rocks obviously contain fossil remains of the most ancient organisms, whereas strata deposited subsequently contain increasingly more recent organic remains, culminating in those of extant plants. Although this "record of rocks" is remarkably long and uninterrupted in such localities as the Grand Canyon, there are few places where such a great series of strata is exposed. Paleobotanists are forced therefore to rely on the exposure of fossil-bearing strata by landslides, washouts, road and rail construction, and, especially, by mining and drilling operations.

In spite of the incompleteness of the fossil record, considerable information has been obtained about plants of the past. Paleobotany has not shed direct light on the origin of life itself, but indirect evidences of its existence, such as calcareous sediments (limestones) and iron ores, are available in strata that are approximately 1½ billion years old (Fig. 6-1). The oldest organisms were aquatic—algal, fungal, and probably bacterial. Many calcareous algae occur in the lower Ordovician strata of the Paleozoic era. The Devonian period of the Paleozoic is strikingly different from earlier strata in that it contains the remains of truly terrestrial plants, including liverworts and representatives of the four lines of seedless vascular plants (Chapters 6, 7). The gradual development of terrestrial plants with vascular tissue indicates the correlation between the migration of plant life to land and the evolution of xylem and phloem. In spite of the rise of the land plants, aquatic algae and fungi have continued to flourish, apparently with little change, until the present.

Sedimentary rocks, of nonmarine origin, of the late Paleozoic (Mississippian and Pennsylvanian) contain a wealth of fossils, some of which have been referred to briefly in earlier chapters. An indirect evidence of the abundance of photosynthetic plants in the Pennsylvanian is the occurrence of extensive deposits of coal in that period. The Pennsylvanian often is called the "age of ferns" because of the abundance of fossilized fern leaves in its strata. Some of these, however, were seed ferns, sometimes considered to be the precursors of the flowering plants. In addition, giant tree-size *Equisetum*-like plants (Fig. 6-14) and others of similar dimensions, resembling somewhat our modern *Lycopodium* and *Selaginella* (Figs. 6-7 and 6-8), flourished in the swamps in Pennsylvanian times. Furthermore, mosses, liverworts, and the remains of tree-like gymnosperms (in addition to seed ferns) are preserved in Pennsylvanian strata. Most of these are still well represented as fossils in Mesozoic strata, but in the Jurassic and Cretaceous periods, especially the latter, the angiosperms appeared and became dominant as the number and diversity of other fossils waned.

We can make several important generalizations on the basis of this brief survey of the fossil record and by inspection of Fig. 6-1.

(1) Indirect and direct evidence indicates that algae, fungi, and bacteria are probably among the most ancient plants, their presence on the earth extending back into the Pre-Cambrian, 1½ billion years ago, and possibly even longer. Similar organisms, with slight modification, are represented in our flora at the present time.

(2) Land plants, probably derived from algae that gradually colonized muddy shores and finally drier habitats, had evolved and become abundant by the Devonian (275 million years ago). The number, complexity, and diversity of Devonian fossilized vascular plants strongly suggest that they must have evolved considerably earlier, although unequivocal evidence of this is lacking.

(3) The widespread occurrence of vascular tissues (xylem and phloem) coincided with colonization of the land.

(4) Successively more recent strata reveal an apparent orderliness of development of representative divisions of plants, the order being, from ancient to recent: the algae, bacteria, and fungi; seedless vascular plants; and, finally, seed plants. Of the latter, the flowering plants are the most recent.

(5) A number of organisms prominent in ancient floras are no longer extant. In most cases, the reasons for their extinction are not clear.

Plant fossils, then, indicate that our present flora is changed in composition from floras of earlier periods of the earth's history. Since we know that living organisms are descendants of living precursors, we conclude from the fossil record that our present plants (and animals, of course) are modified descendants of more ancient ones. This, in essence, is what is meant by evolution. All modern biologists accept this point of view. It is when individual biologists attempt to outline the *course* of evolution and thus to draw up the actual phylogenetic lines of descent, especially among the taxa more comprehensive than genera, that they often disagree, because they interpret evidences differently.

Anyone who surveys the comparative morphology of living plants in the light of the paleobotanical record usually becomes convinced that terrestrial plants have evolved from aquatic algal precursors, and that the primitive, spore-bearing, seedless vascular plants which grew upon the earth from the Devonian through the late Paleozoic periods have now themselves been crowded into near oblivion by the flowering plants that have been dominant since the Cretaceous. What will occur in plant life in the millions of years ahead is open to speculation. The changes are occurring at present, inexorably, but the framework of our human life-span clouds our perception of the long-range events yet to transpire in the evolutionary process.

SELECTED READINGS

Alexopoulos, C. J., *Introductory Mycology*. New York: Wiley, 1962. A well-illustrated general account of the fungi.

Andrews, H. N., *Studies in Paleobotany*. New York: Wiley, 1961. A survey of fossil plants and their relationships with extant forms; includes an introduction to palynology.

Benson, L., *Plant Classification*. Boston: Heath, 1957. A comprehensive treatment of the classification of *vascular plants* and of the criteria on which the classification is based. Included also are instructions on identifying plants and preserving specimens. The book closes with a consideration of some aspects of plant ecology and the floras of North America.

Bold, H. C., *Morphology of Plants*. New York: Harper, 1957. A summary of plant structure and reproduction with reference to algae, fungi, liverworts, mosses, and vascular plants, both seed-bearing and non-seed-bearing. Includes a discussion of systems of classification and of plants of the past.

Delevoryas, T., *Morphology and Evolution of Fossil Plants*. New York: Holt, Rinehart and Winston, 1962. A brief treatment of the nature of fossil floras.

Eames, A. J., *Morphology of the Angiosperms*. New York: McGraw-Hill, 1961. A comprehensive treatment at an advanced level of the anatomy and reproductive process in the flowering plants.

Esau, K., *Plant Anatomy*. New York: Wiley, 1953. A detailed and comprehensive account of the gross and minute structure of vascular plants, with copious illustrations.

Foster, A. F., and E. M. Gifford, Jr., *Comparative Morphology of Vascular Plants*. San Francisco: Freeman, 1959. A summary, at a somewhat advanced level, of the structure and reproduction of vascular plants and a discussion of general topics in plant morphology.

Smith, G. M., *Cryptogamic Botany,* Vols. I and II. New York: McGraw-Hill, 1955. A two-volume, advanced-level treatment of representative algae, fungi, liverworts, mosses, ferns, and other seedless vascular plants.

Stanier, R. Y., and M. Doudoroff, and E. A. Adelberg, *The Microbial World,* 2nd ed. Englewood Cliffs, N. J.: Prentice-Hall, 1963. A comprehensive introduction to microbiology.

Index

Abscission layer, 56
Accessory cell, 54
Acetic acid, 24
Achlya, 29–32, 105, 106:
  A. ambisexualis, 32, 105, 106
Adiantum, 54, 71, 72:
  A. capillus-veneris, 71
Aecia, 35
Aeciospores, 35
"Age of ferns," 108
Algae, 2, 3, 7–19, 27, 28, 76, 77, 102, 103, 104, 105, 108, 109:
  blue-green, 4, 5, 8, 10, 12, 16–17
  brown, 10
  cellular organization, 12
  defined, 7–8
  filamentous, 10
  as food, 8
  form and organization of, 9–12
  golden, 10
  green, 10, 11
  habitat of, 8
  hydrocolloids of, 8
  leaf-like, 10
  life cycles, 15
  membranous, 10
  nitrogen fixation by, 8, 17
  planktonic, 8
  red, 10
  reproduction in, 12–16
  sexual reproduction in, 12–16
  toxicity of, 8
  tubular, 10
Algin, 8
Allergies, 92
Alternation of generations, 15, 60
Amebae, 26, 27
Amino acids, 107
Anabaena, 16, 17
Angiosperms, 3, 18, 58, 77, 87–101, 109
Angiospermy, 79, 101
Annual plants, 92
  defined, 47
Annual ring, 52, 53
Annulus, 73, 74
Anther, 89, 92, 94, 101
Antheridium, 11, 31, 41, 44, 60, 61, 68, 74, 75
Anthoceros, 45
Anthophyta, 3
Antibotics, *defined,* 24
Antipodal cell, 95, 97

Apical cell, 68
Apogamy, 75
Apple, 88
Archegonium, 41, 44, 60, 61, 64, 65, 68, 74, 75, 83, 84, 95, 107
Aristolochia, 50
Arthrophyta, 3
Arthrophytes, 3, 5, 8, 65–69, 70, 76, 77, 102
Ascocarp, 29, 33
Ascomycetes, 3, 28–29, 30
Ascomycota, 3
Ascospore, 29, 33
Ascus, 28, 29
Asexual reproduction, 12, 13, 104
Asparagus, 88
Aspergillus, 32, 33
Aureomycin, 24
Autumnal coloration, 56
Axenic culture, 22
Azolla, 76

Bacillariophyceae, 19
Bacillus, 21, 22
Bacitracin, 24
Bacteria, 2, 3, 4, 21–24, 109:
  fossil, 24
  harmful, 23
  nitrifying, 23
  pathogenic, 23
  photosynthetic, 23
Bacteriophage, 24
Bananas, 88
Barberry, 35
Bark, 52
Basal cell, 98
Basidiocarp, 35, 36
Basidiomycetes, 3, 29, 30
Basidiomycota, 3
Basidiospore, 30, 35, 36
Basidium, 30, 35, 36
Basswood, 53
Beans, 99
Bees, 95
Beets, 88
Berberis vulgaris, 35
Berries, 88
Binary fission, 104
Bird's nest fungus, 29
Bisexual plants, 105
Black mold, 32–33

Blastophaga, 95
Bog moss, 39
Bracken fern, 72
Broccoli, 88
Brown algae, 103
Bryophyta, 3
Bud, 48, 49, 79, 88:
  axillary, 49
  covered, 82
Bud scale, 48
Budding 29
Butterflies, 96

Cabbage, 88
Cacti, 88
Calamites, 66, 76
Calamophyton, 76
Calvatia, 29
Calyptra, 42
Calyx, 88
Cambium, 48, 52, 53, 78
Capitulum, 91, 92
Capsella, 98
Capsule, 42, 44
Carpel, 87, 90
Carrageenin, 8
Carrots, 88
Cauliflower, 88
Cedar, 85
Celery, 88
Cell division, 104
Cell republic, 103
Cell wall, 4, 13
Cellular organization, 4, 107
Cellulose, 10, 28
Charophyta, 3, 10
Cheese, 24
Chemoautotrophic, 23
Chitin, 28
Chlamydomonadaceae, 9
Chlamydomonas, 9, 12–15, 105, 106:
  C. eugametos, 9
  C. moewusii, 105
Chlorella, 11
Chlorophyceae, 9
Chlorophyll *a*, 10, 107
Chlorophyll *b*, 10
Chlorophyll *c*, 10
Chlorophyll *d*, 10
Chlorophyta, 3, 10, 11, 17
Chloroplast, 4, 12, 13
Chromosomes, 5
Chroococcus, 17
Chrysophyta, 3, 10, 11, 19
Chytrids, 28
Cilia, 9
Circinate vernation, 71, 85
Citrus fruits, 88
Cladophora, 11, 12
Class, 9, 107
Classification, 2, 3, 28, 78, 106–110:
  artificial, 2
  natural, 2, 106
  phylogenetic, 2, 106–107
Clonal culture, 13

Club mosses, 3, 58, 61–65, 68, 70, 76, 77, 78, 102
Coal, 108
Coccus, 21
Coleus blumei, 49
Colonies, 9, 10
Columella, 33
Companion cell, 50, 52
Comparative biochemistry, 107
Comparative morphology, 107
Compound leaves, 72
Compound pistil, 87, 89–91
Cone, 78
Conifer, 3, 82, 93, 107
Coniferophyta, 3
Contractile vacuole, 12, 13
Cork, 88
Corn, 88, 91, 98, 100
Corolla, 88
Cortex, 48, 51, 52, 60
Coscinodiscus, 19
Cotyledon, 75, 84, 98, 99, 100
Cretaceous period, 58, 109, 110
Cryptogamae, 3
Cucurbita, 52
Cup fungi, 28, 29
Cuticle, 51
Cutin, 51
Cuttings, 104
Cyanophycean starch, 10
Cyanophyta, 3, 10, 12, 16–17
Cycadophyta, 3
Cycas revoluta, 85
Cycads, 3, 78, 82, 85, 86, 93, 107
Cyperus, 54
Cypress, 78, 85

Daisies, 78
Darwin, 2
Dasya, 18
Decay, 21, 24
Deciduous plants, 56
Devonian period, 57, 58, 59, 76, 108, 109, 110
Diachea, 24
Diatomaceous earth, 8, 19
Diatoms, 8, 19
Dictyostelium, 26, 27
Differentiation, 47
Dinoflagellates, 10
Dioon, 85
Diploid state, 44, 105, 106
Disc flower, 91, 92
DNA, 5, 12, 17, 22
Double fertilization, 94, 96–97, 98, 101
Dryopteris, 71–75
Division, 3, 9, 107
Duckweed, 47, 88

Egg, 11, 31, 74, 81, 84, 94, 97, 105
Egg cell, 95
Egg nucleus, 97
Elater, 67, 68
Elm, 78

Elodea, 88
Embryo, 65, 84, 85, 94, 98, 99, 101
Embryogeny, 92, 97–99
Embryophyta, 3
Endodermis, 50, 51, 61
Endoplasmic reticulum, 4
Endosperm, 94, 98, 101
Enzyme, 2, 23, 28, 32, 37
Epicotyl, 99, 100
Epidermis, 52, 60
Epidermal hairs, 53
Equisetum, 64, 65–69, 72, 76, 78, 104, 105:
   E. arvense, 67, 68
   E. hyemale, 67, 68
Equisetum-like plants, 108
Escherichia coli, 23
Eucalyptus, 47
Euglena, 17, 18
Euglenophyta, 3, 10, 12, 17, 19
Euonymus, 54
Evergreen plants, 56
Evolution, 5, 6, 57, 95, 109–110

Family, 9, 107
Fermentation, 29
Ferns, 2, 3, 58, 70–76, 77, 78, 102, 104, 105, 106:
   heterosporous, 75
   maidenhair, 54
Fertilization, 42, 68, 82, 84, 95, 96–97
Fiber, 50, 51
"Fiddle head," 71
Figs, 95
Filament, 10, 89, 92
Fir, 78, 85
Flagella, 9, 13
Floridean starch, 10
Flower, 88–93
Flowering plants, 3, 58, 77, 87–101, 109
Fossil, 59, 65, 76, 78, 107, 108–110
Fossil record, 107
Fragmentation, 104
Fruit, 77, 79, 87, 92, 97–100, 101
Frustule, 19
Fucus, 12, 17, 18, 105, 106
Funaria, 39, 40, 41, 43, 44
Functional megaspore, 81, 93, 94, 96
Fungi, 2, 3, 27–37, 77, 102, 104, 105, 106, 107, 109:
   algal, 3, 28
   classification, 3, 28
   club, 28
   cup, 28, 29
   fruiting, 29
   hallucinogenic, 37
   pore, 29
   sac, 3, 28
   sexual reproduction in, 32
   shelf, 28, 29
Fungi Imperfecti, 3, 28

Gametangium, 28, 40
Gamete, 13, 14, 15, 26, 28, 105, 106
Gametogenesis, 92, 93–95

Gametophyte, 46, 60, 61, 63, 65, 68, 73, 74, 75, 93, 101, 105, 106:
   female, 64, 65, 66, 80, 83, 84, 89, 94, 95, 96, 97, 98
   male, 64, 65, 80, 81, 83, 84, 89, 93, 94, 95, 97
Gap, leaf 70
Genetics, 5
Generative cell, 94, 95, 97
Genus, 9
Geographical distribution, 107
Geologic time, 58
Germ, 99
Germination, 40, 74, 84, 97, 101
Gills, 35
Ginkgo, 3, 82, 85, 86, 93
Ginkgophyta, 3, 86
Glandular hairs, 51
Gnetophyta, 3
Golgi bodies, 4
Gonyaulax, 9
Grand Canyon, 108
Grape, 88
Grasses, 88
Ground meristem, 49
Ground pine, 62
Growth, 12, 103:
   apical, 104
   generalized, 103
   localized, 12
Guard cell, 51, 54, 60
Gymnospermae, 3, 77
Gymnosperms, 77–86, 88, 96, 98, 101, 109
Gymnospermy, 79, 101

"Hair cap" moss, 39
Haploid state, 15, 105, 106
Haustoria, 28
Helianthus, 93
Hemlock, 78
Hepatophyta, 3
Hermaphroditic plants, 105
Heterogamy, 13, 14, 105
Heterosporous plants, 106
Heterospory, 64, 65, 80, 106
Heterothallic organisms, 13, 105
Heterothallism, 65
Heterotrophic plants, 20
"Higher plants," 103
Holdfast, 104
Holozoic, 21
Homosporous plants, 64, 68, 106
Homothallic organisms, 13, 74, 105
Homothallism, 105
Hormones, sexual, 31, 32
Horned liverwort, 45
"Horsetails," 3, 65
Hyacinth, 88
Hyphae, 27
Hypocotyl, 98, 99

Igneous rocks, 107
Inheritance, 107

Imperfect flower, 91
Indusium, 72, 73:
  false, 72
  true, 72
Inflorescence, 88, 91, 92
Integument, 81, 89, 94, 96, 97, 98, 99
Intercalary meristem, 104
International Code of Botanical Nomenclature, 3, 9
Internode, 48, 66, 67, 68
Iris, 78, 88
Isoetes, 62, 64, 76:
  I. lithophila, 62
Isogametes, 105
Isogamous gametes, 14

Juniper, 78
Jurassic period, 58, 109

Kelps, 11, 17, 103, 104

Lactic acid, 24
Laminarin, 10
Laminaria, 18
Lamproderma, 24
Land plants, 106, 109
Larch, 85
Leaf, 53–56, 68, 75, 76, 100, 104:
  compound, 55
  macrophyllous, 76
  microphyllous, 76
  primary, 75
  primordia, 53
  simple, 55
Lederberg, 23
Lemna, 47, 88
Lepidodendron, 65, 66, 76
Lettuce, 88
Leucolejeunea, 45
Leucosin, 10
Lichens, 3, 28, 29, 34
Life, origin of, 6
Life cycles, 15, 43, 107
Ligustrum, 54, 55
Lilac, 78
Lilium, 94, 96
Lily, 88, 94, 96, 97
Linear tetrad, 93, 94, 96
Lip cells, 73, 74
Liverworts, 3, 38, 44, 45, 46, 64, 77, 102, 103, 104, 107, 108, 109:
  origin of, 46–47
Locule, 99
"Lower plants," 103
Luciferase, 37
Luciferin, 37
Luminescence, mushroom, 37
Lycopodium, 61–65, 66, 76, 105, 108

Macrophyllous leaf, 70, 76, 104
Maidenhair tree, 3, 85
Mannitol, 10

Maple, 78
Marsilea, 72, 75, 76
Megasporangium, 64, 65, 81, 82, 84, 89, 92, 94, 96, 97, 98, 106
Megaspore, 64, 65, 66, 80, 82, 89, 93, 94, 96, 106
Megaspore mother cell, 83
Megasporocyte, 64, 81, 93, 94, 96
Megasporogenesis, 92, 93
Megasporophyll, 64, 74, 87, 88, 89, 91, 93, 96, 101
Megastrobilus, 79, 83
Meiosis, 5, 15, 26, 33, 36, 59, 60, 63, 64, 68, 72, 92, 93, 95, 104, 106, 107:
  sporic, 60
Melon, 88
Mesophyll, 72:
  palisade, 55
  spongy, 55
Mesozoic era, 58, 109
Metabolism, 4, 107
Micron, 21
Microphyllophyta, 3, 104
Microphyllous leaf, 62, 70, 76, 104
Micropyle, 81, 83, 89, 94, 96, 97, 101
Microsporangium, 64, 80, 82, 92, 94, 95, 96, 101
Microspore, 64, 65, 78, 82, 83, 84, 89, 92, 94, 95, 106
Microspore mother cell, 82, 92
Microsporocyte, 82, 92, 94
Microsporogenesis, 92
Microsporophyll, 63, 64, 80, 82, 88, 89, 90, 91
Microstrobilus, 86
Mildew, powdery, 28
Mississippian period, 58, 108
Mitochondrion, 4
Mitosis, 15
Mnium, 41
Molds, 28, 32–34:
  brown, green, and pink, 28
  water, 28
Morchella, 29
Morel, 28, 29
Morning glory, 78
Mosses, 2, 3, 38–44, 46, 64, 76, 77, 102, 103, 104, 105, 107, 109:
  life cycle, 43
  origin of, 46–47
Mulberry, 91
Multicellular organism, 103
Mushroom, 28, 29, 35–37:
  life cycle, 36
Mutations, 5, 107
Mycelium, 27, 28, 32, 33, 34:
  primary, 36
  secondary, 36
Myxomycetes, 3, 24–27
Myxomycota, 3

Natural selection, 107
Navicula, 19
Nectar, 96
Nemalion, 18

Neurospora, 34
Nidularia, 29
Nitrobacter, 23
Nitrogen fixation, 17:
  bacterial, 24
Nitrosomonas, 23
Node, 48, 66, 67, 68
Nonvascular plants, 38, 39
Nucleolus, 12
Nucleus, 4, 13

Oak, 78
Oak wood, 51
Obligate parasite, 34
Oedogonium, 11
Oenothera, 96
Oil, 10
"Old man's beard," 34
Onion, 88
Ontogeny, 103
Oogamy, 13, 105
Oogonium, 11
Operculum, 42
Ophioglossum vulgatum, 72
Orchids, 99
Order, 9, 107
Ordovician period, 58, 108
Organization, 102–104
Origin of life, 6
Oscillatoria, 11, 17
Ovary, 89, 90, 93, 99, 100
Ovule, 80, 81, 82, 83, 84, 86, 89, 90, 93, 94, 95, 96, 97, 99, 101

Paleobotany, 108
Paleozoic era, 58, 108, 110
Palynology, 92
Pandorina, 104
Paramylon, 10
Parasite, 20, 34
Parallel evolution, 57
Parsnip, 88
Parthenogenesis, 16
Pea, 79, 99, 100
Peanut, 99
Pear, 88
Peat moss, 39
Pectin, 10
Peduncle, 99
Penicillin, 34
Penicillium, 32–34:
  P. chrysogenum, 33, 34
Pennsylvanian period, 58, 65, 66, 108, 109
Perennial plants, 40, 47, 71, 92
Pericycle, 50, 51
Periderm, 52, 53
Peristome, 42, 43, 44
Petal, 88, 89, 90, 97
Petiole, 55, 72, 88
Petrifaction, 108
Phacus, 19
Phaeophyta, 3, 10, 11, 17, 18
Phagotrophic, 21
Phanerogamae, 3

Phloem, 11, 38, 46, 48, 50, 52, 72, 77, 103, 104, 108, 109:
  primary, 50, 53
  secondary, 52
Photoautotrophic plants, 20, 23
Photosynthesis, 6, 8, 20, 55, 68
Phycocyanin, 10
Phycoerythrin, 10
Phycomycetes, 3, 28
Phylogeny, 57
Phylum, 3
Physarum polycephalum, 25
Pine, 78, 79, 82–85
Pinus, 82–85:
  P. strobus, 51
  P. virginiana, 81, 84
  wood, 51
"Pipes," 67
Pistil, 87, 88, 89, 97, 99, 101:
  compound, 87, 89–91
  simple, 87, 89
Pistillate flower, 91, 92
Pith, 48, 50, 53
Plant body, organization of, 102–104
Plasma membrane, 4
Plasmodium, 25, 26
Plumule, 99
Polar nuclei, 94, 95, 97
Pollen, 89, 96
Pollen chamber, 81, 83, 84
Pollen grain, 81, 83, 84, 92, 93, 95, 96, 97
Pollen tube, 81, 84, 85, 89, 93, 96
Pollen sac, 95
Pollination, 81, 83, 89, 92, 93, 95–96, 97, 101
Pollination droplet, 83, 84
Polymyxin-B, 24
Polyploid state, 43
Polyporus, 29
Polytrichum, 39, 40, 43, 105
Pond scum, 7
Poplar, 91
Poppy, 90
Potatoes, 88
Pore fungus, 29
Pre-Cambrian era, 58, 109
Primary endosperm nucleus, 97, 98
Primary permanent tissues, 50
Primary root, 100
Primary tissues, 48
Primitive condition, 103, 105
Procambium, 49
Promeristem, 49
Pronuba, 96
Prothallium, 73
Prothallus, 73
Protista, 9
Protoderm, 49
Protonema, 40
Protoplasmic connection, 10
Psalliota campestris, 29, 36
Pseudoplasmodium, 26, 27
Psilocybe Mexicana, 37
Psilophyta, 3, 76, 104
Psilophytes, 3, 58, 59–61, 68, 70, 76, 77, 102
Psilophyton, 59

Psilotum, 64, 68, 76:
  P. nudum, 59–61
Pteridium, 72
Pteridophyta, 3, 76
Pterophyta, 3
Pteropsida, 3, 78
Puccinia graminis, 34–35:
  life cycle, 35
Puffball, 28, 29
Pure culture, 22
Pyrenoid, 13
Pyrrophyta, 3, 10

Quaking bog, 39
Quercus velutina, 51
Quillwort, 62

Rachis, 72
Radicle, 98, 99, 100, 101
Ranunculus, 50
Ray, 51:
  vascular, 53
Ray flower, 91, 92
Receptacle, 72, 88, 89, 90, 97
Recombination, 107
Red eye spot, 12
Red tide, 9
Reduction, 53, 103
Reduction division, 5
Redwood trees, 47
Reproduction, 12–16, 104–106:
  asexual, 12, 104
  sexual, 12–16, 104
Reproductive cycles, 15
Reproductive phenomena, 107
Rhizoid, 28, 32, 39, 59, 60, 64, 67, 68, 73, 104
Rhizome, 39, 59, 60, 68, 104
Rhizopus, 10, 32, 33, 105, 106:
  R. stolonifer, 32, 33
Rhodophyta, 3, 10, 17, 18
Rhoeo discolor, 54
Rhubarb, 88
Rhynia, 76:
  R. Gwynne-Vaughani, 59
Riccia, 45, 104
Rice, 88
Rockweeds, 17, 18
Root, 39, 48, 50, 51, 88, 104:
  embryonic, 100
  primary, 100
Root-cap, 48, 49
Root hairs, 51, 53
Rose, 78
Rusts, 30, 34
Rye, 88

Saccharomyces cerevisiae, 30
Salvinia, 70, 75, 76
Saprolegnia, 30
Saprophytic plants, 20–21
Scheffeleria, 54
Schizomycota, 3

Schleiden, M. J., 4
Schwann, T., 4
"Scouring rushes," 66
Sea lettuce, 11, 12, 104, 106
Secondary growth, 52
Secondary tissues, 52
Sedimentary rocks, 107
Seed, 77, 82, 84, 85, 92, 94, 96, 97–100
Seed coat, 84, 94, 98, 100
Seed dormancy, 101
Seed ferns, 78, 108, 109
Seedless vascular plants, 102, 107, 108, 109
Seedings 85, 100
Seed plants, 2, 77–101, 105, 106, 109:
  angiosperms, 87–101
  gymnospermous, 77–86
Segregation, 107
Selaginella, 61–65, 66, 72, 75, 76, 80, 82, 83, 104, 105, 106, 108
  S. Kraussiana, 63
  S. Sprengeri, 63
Selection, 5
Sepals, 88, 89, 90, 99
Sequoia, 47, 52
Sequoiadendron, 47, 52
Seta, 42
Sexuality, 107
Sexual reproduction, 4, 5, 12–16, 28, 32, 35, 36, 37, 97, 104, 107:
  origin of, 104
Shelf fungus, 29
Shepherd's purse, 98
Shield fern, 71, 73, 74, 75
Sieve cell, 50
Sieve plate, 52
Sieve tube, 50, 52
Sigillaria, 65, 66, 76
Silicon, 10
Slime molds, 24–27:
  cellular, 26–27
  life cycle of, 26
Smuts, 30
Sophora, 54
Sorus, 72
"Spawn," mushroom, 36
Species, 9, 107
Sperm, 11, 41, 42, 60, 68, 81, 84, 86, 94, 105:
  cell, 97
  nucleus, 97
Spermagonium, 35
Spermatophyta, 3
Sphaerocarpos, 45
Sphagnum, 37, 39
Sphenophyllum, 66, 76
Sphenopsids, 3
Spike mosses, 3, 58, 61–65, 70
Spinach, 88
Spirillum, 22
Spirogyra, 11, 12
Sporangium, 42, 54, 59, 60, 62, 67, 68, 72, 73, 74
Sporangiophore, 32, 33, 67, 68
Spore, 15, 40, 59, 68, 73:
  bacterial, 22
  slime mold, 26

Spore mother cell, 42, 59, 60
Sporocyte, 42, 59, 60, 62, 64, 68, 72
Sporogenesis, 83, 92–93
Sporogenous cells, 62
Sporogenous tissue, 68, 72
Sporophyll, 61, 88, 89
Sporophyte, 42, 44, 46, 47, 59, 60, 74, 75, 78, 81, 95, 106
Spruce, 77, 85
Spur shoot, 82, 86
Squash, 88
Stamen, 89, 90, 92, 96, 97
Staminate flower, 91, 92
Starch, 4, 10, 107
Stele, 50
Stem, 48, 104
Stigma, 12, 13, 89, 90, 93, 95, 96, 99, 101
Stomata, 51, 54, 55, 60, 72
Streptomycin, 24
Strobilus, 61, 62, 63, 65, 67, 68, 78, 79, 88, 93
Style, 89, 93, 99
Subtilin, 24
Suspensor, 85, 98
Synergid, 94, 97

Teliospore, 35
Terramycin, 24
Tetrad, 64, 68, 93, 94, 95
Thallophyta, 3
Tilia Americana, 53
Toadstool, 35
Tomato, 78, 79, 88, 99
Traces, 48, 70
Tracheid, 48, 50, 51, 72, 82
Trachelomonas, 19
Tracheophyta, 3, 57
"Trailing evergreen," 62
Tree fern, 70, 72
Triceratium, 19
Tube cell, 94, 95, 97
Tube nucleus, 94
Turnips, 88
Tyrothricin, 24

Ulva, 11, 12, 104, 106
Unisexual plants, 105
Urediniospore, 35
Usnea, 34

Vacuole, 4, 12
Vascular plants, 38, 46–101, 104, 105, 109:
    seed-bearing, 77–86
    seedless, 57–76
Vascular tissue, 38, 46, 48, 52, 53, 57, 59, 70, 76, 109:
    defined, 38
Vaucheria, 11
Vegetable, 88
Vein, 72
Venation, 54, 55
"Venus maidenhair," 71
Vernation, circinate, 71
Vessel, xylem, 48, 50, 52, 72
Viruses, 24
Volvocales, 9
Volvox, 10, 11, 105

Wasps, 95, 96
Water lilies, 88
Water molds, 28, 29–32
Wheat, 88
Wheat rust, 34–35
Whisk fern, 59
White pine wood, 51
Willow, 91, 92
Wood, 51, 82

Xylem, 38, 46, 48, 50, 51, 72, 77, 103, 108, 109:
    primary, 50, 53
    secondary 52, 53, 66, 78, 82
    spring, 51
    summer, 51

Yeasts, 28
Yucca, 96
Yucca moth, 96

Zamia, 85
Zea mays, 49, 52, 98, 100
Zoosporangium, 31, 32
Zoospore, 12, 17, 28, 32, 104
Zygote, 13, 14, 15, 24, 26, 42, 47, 60, 64, 68, 74, 84, 98, 103, 105, 106
Zymase, 30